MAKING THE MEDIA REVOLUTION

MAKING THE MEDIA REVOLUTION

A Handbook for Video-Tape Production

PETER WEINER

Illustrations by WILLIAM BAYLIS

Macmillan Publishing Co., Inc.
New York

Collier Macmillan Publishers
London

Macmillan Publishing Co., Inc.
Collier-Macmillan Canada Ltd.

Library of Congress Catalog Card Number: 72-92867
FIRST PRINTING
Printed in the United States of America

To Barbara

ACKNOWLEDGMENTS

I wish to thank James Tick for some appreciated photographs; Virginia Johnson and especially Lillian Varsames for typing the manuscript; Allan Miller for his technical assistance; Richard Knabel for the generous donation of office space; Robert Pfannkuch for permission to reprint his essay "The Television Signal" as Appendix D to this book; Robert Hochstein for editorial assistance; Union Free School District Number Three in Hawthorne, N.Y., for the use of their facilities; and my wife Barbara for her encouragement and assistance.

CONTENTS

Contents

THE MEDIA REVOLUTION

The young people who have experienced a decade of television have naturally imbibed an urge toward involvement in depth that makes all the remote visualized goals of usual culture not only unreal, but irrelevant, and not only irrelevant but anemic. It is the total involvement in all-inclusive *nowness* that occurs in young lives via TV's mosaic image. This change in attitude has nothing to do with programming in any way, and would be the same if the program consisted entirely of the highest cultural content. The change in attitude by means of relating themselves to the mosaic TV image would occur in any event. It is, of course, not only our job to understand this change, but to exploit it for its pedagogical richness. The TV child expects involvement and doesn't want a specialist *job* in the future. He does want a *role* and a deep commitment to his society.

Education is civil defense against media fallout.

Marshall McLuhan
Understanding Media, p. 292

Marshall McLuhan is not offering a call to revolution here. He is merely saying that the revolution has already occurred, and it is about time that we recognized this fact. Children today are not following their parent's middle-class concept of the American Dream. They have their own notion of a dream that is just as American in concept as the one of their parents. They yearn for involvement, but not in terms of becoming involved in corporate affairs. Their dream encompasses society on a worldwide scale.

American tourists walk around Europe with Instamatic cameras capturing their experiences on film, to make the trip seem more real.

They never seem to be comfortable or satisfied by the experience in person. In order to prove that they were actually there, and to make the experience of seeing something "live" an experience that they can deal with, they must photograph it. Once the sights are safely captured on film, the tourist can then relax back at his hotel. Europeans see this going on and can't understand why the American doesn't just enjoy the view instead of hoping his picture came out all right. Some people never really see things, except as an exposure reading.

You see very little mixing between American tourists and their middle-aged European counterparts. On the other hand, wherever you go, you will see young people from all countries enjoying one another as well as the sights. There is a definite sense of global ties among youth; they share many of the same feelings and attitudes. The Generation Gap doesn't exist only in America; it is a worldwide phenomenon. The main reason for this is the media. Young people accept the media for what they are. They share experiences with other cultures every time they see a film or watch television. This flow of information never existed before, so we are experiencing a new phenomenon, which few people have yet to accept. One thing that the Media Revolution is accomplishing is to bring people of different cultures together. It enables them to meet without initial distrust, and gives them common grounds for the sharing of values and ideas. The "Global Village" is rapidly becoming a reality.

The Media Revolution is already upon us, but most educators are unaware of it. They are still teaching in formal classrooms, and they are still teaching with the same traditions that were used to teach their grandparents. One reason for so many young people's discontent with their schools is that the schools are not teaching with a media consciousness. To be able to fully operate in today's American society, one must be totally aware of what role the media are playing, and how information can be obtained from them in the most efficient manner. Schools are not preparing visually literate children, and media illiterates cannot function in society with a high degree of success.

When a new medium comes along, certain things are bound to happen. The one thing that will invariably occur is that most people will think of the new medium as a different form of an already existing medium. Radio is a "talking telegraph," television

is "radio with pictures," and a 747 is just a "big 707." Nomenclature
is a handy way of determining how this is occurring. Automobiles
were called "horseless carriages," and steam engines were called
"iron horses."

This leads us to the next kind of misconception that occurs,
and that is that people always think that they know *what* the new
medium is all about, but they never really understand *how* it will
change society. The telegraph was first used for things like lotteries
and remote chess games. Early radio never carried commercials.
It was just used by enthusiasts who talked to each other, and
occasionally it entertained whoever was listening. Surely, very few
people in the early twenties could have envisioned the giant corpora-
tions that have sprung up because of radio. There is no need to
even describe the naïveté of the terms "horseless carriage" and "iron
horse." Suffice it to say that America would not resemble what
this country is today, if the railroads were always just thought
of as strong horses. How different the landscape would be if cars
remained merely "horseless carriages"!

A new medium either drastically changes the purposes of an
older medium, or completely eliminates it. Before Gutenberg invented movable type, the only books were the illuminated texts,
carefully hand-produced by monks. After a period of time illuminated texts ceased to exist. There was no longer a need for them,
and since the job of printing could be done so much more quickly
and efficiently by the printing press, the demand died down. Soon,
the only illuminated texts around were in museums. No one ever
thought of hand-printed books as a passing phase. That was how
books were printed. Movable type was first thought of as fast
printing, certainly not a medium that could be and would be used
to change the world's society. Movable type and the printing press
were the greatest means of information access ever to have taken
place until television.

An example of how a new medium can change the function of
an old one is seen in radio. Before television became so omnipotent,
radio was the main way by which most people were entertained.
Families gathered in front of the radio and listened intently to the
adventures of "The Shadow" and "The Lone Ranger." Today, no
one knows what function radio is serving. Nobody really *listens*
to radio. It is used mainly to fill up empty houses with sound, or

to provide a background to the tactile experience of driving a car. Radio certainly carries none of the importance it had during World War II, for example.

An example of this type of misconception is taking place right now in the airline industry. The introduction of the 747 "jumbo jets" was a much heralded event. Yet, today, many people refuse to fly in them, because they are too big. The problem lies in the faulty concept of the 747 as being no more than just a "big jet." It really is much more than that. The 747 is capable of transporting many people very inexpensively. If television has allowed us to interface our culture with other cultures around the world electronically, then the 747 can let us do it in person. A fully loaded 747 could carry passengers to Europe for under $100, round trip. Virtually anyone could afford that, and the airlines could still make a profit. They can't reduce the fares now, say the airlines, because the ground facilities can't handle the crowds of people that would be created by the passengers and their friends. What better way of information dissemination could you have than inexpensive trips to the location of the original source of whatever information one may be curious about?

Most people take television for granted. The physiological effects that the medium has on the viewing public, or the number of boxes of soap powder it can sell, have been studied and defined many times. What people take for granted is that the thing works. Very few of us ever wonder about that image on the screen and how it gets there.

Before television became a consumer-oriented product in the late 1940s, many people had read that a new device, "tele-vision," was on the way. This medium had been around since 1928, and quite a few people were aware of it from the start, but not the general public. One can assume that the reason for this was that the big electronic manufacturers had not as yet exploited radio to the saturation point. Technology is always way ahead of consumer goods. (Although now, in our technologically oriented society, the period of time from research and development to actual product sales has been reduced considerably.)

An example of how the manufacturers' thinking works is that the capacity for stereo has been around for a long time. Yet, the consumer had to first buy a big deluxe model record player. Then, hi-fi came along. The consumer then had to buy a high fidelity set. The manufacturers let hi-fi last for a couple of years, and then they let stereo come out. Once again, the poor consumer, after spending his cash on the latest "state of the art" device, found out that all of his beloved sound system was obsolete.

The same thing happened with FM stereo. It has always been known that the FM signal could carry two channels. However, since sales of FM receivers had been lagging, the industrial complex decided to drop stereo broadcasting on us, and now the sales of FM stereo receivers are skyrocketing.

All of the above is conjecture, of course, but when one looks at the relation of an item to the sale, and the frequency of "new" developments in a particular product line, one can make certain observations.

At any rate, once the manufacturers felt that radio had reached a pinnacle in sales, they concluded it was time to drop a new kind of radio on us—radio that you can see! They started to circulate bits of information about this device, but so little was actually known about this medium that many people thought "tele-vision" was a visual telephone, or what we now call the "picture-phone." Not many people were too sure about what they were getting into, and this included the early broadcasters. Milton Berle and wrestling lasted only long enough to get a large number of sets sold. When people really began to think of television as a new *medium,* instead of a new form of an old medium (radio that has pictures), this type of programming died out. Unfortunately, many producers of broadcast television fare have still not realized this fact, and we viewers are suffering the consequences. "Me and the Chimp," is no longer on the air, but Johnny Carson is. Since nobody was really sure what they were getting into when television got its start, we are saddled with the greatest means of transmitting information ever developed, in the most technologically oriented country in the world, yet most people still think of it as radio with pictures!

European television has shown us that the medium does not have to be the way it is in this country, as evidenced by the fact that more and more "Emmies" are being won by British television programs every year. This also shows, however, that people are beginning to realize that they can do new and better things with video than they thought possible. "Laugh-in" is a perfect example. Although already trite, that format was a totally new style, and has since drastically changed television's image. The development of portable television cameras and video tape recorders will do more to hasten the end of broadcast television as it now exists, than all the "Laugh-in's" put together. High-quality portable video is being recognized early as a new medium, and not just as "portable television."

Since the easiest way to describe this new medium is to call it "portable television," we shall continue to do so, but let us interject some new nomenclature. *Electrography,* as defined in the introduction, is the art or process of producing images and sound on magnetic (video) tape, in synchronization with each other. We feel that electrography will be the main tool for media revolutionaries to use. Porta-Pak systems are easy to use, and have just as much, if not more, effect on the viewer as broadcast television. Information can be gathered and displayed instantaneously, and programs can be shown to one person or communally experienced by millions.

The Media Revolution is here, but most of the revolutionaries are unaware that they are performing such a function. There are no clearly defined goals to this revolution; it is a conceptual event. People must be made aware of the revolution, and must become equipped to deal with it. The tools are here, but not the skills.

It will be hard to make many people aware of the changes going on around them, since they are not willing to accept something that they cannot imagine themselves. You may have heard the story about the land full of blind people. In this land, a man with one eye would never be made king, even though it is obvious to us that he should be a leader of some kind. Yet, he would only be considered a raving madman. People with "vision" are not trusted by those who cannot see.

Although the Media Revolution is certainly not a political one, the results will prove to have affected the political system, as well as just about every facet of our life-style as we now know it. When instant communication and access to information is made available to everyone, and when entire populations are wired into one another, some drastic changes are bound to happen. One can easily foresee the decline in influence that the automobile, the telephone, and the shopping center will have on the American way of life, once the effects of the new media begin to take hold.

One thing which the revolution is not out to accomplish, is the death of print. Print is still the most widely used method of information storage and distribution. There is still much disagreement among the people who claim to understand what the revolution is all about. McLuhan claims that television is a "cool" medium, and print, a very "hot" one. Others say that print serves society as "television's Thorazine" (Shamberg, p. 7). Reading, they say, can calm you down after a hard day of television watching. There is a vast difference of opinion in those widely varying statements.

In my opinion, no one is qualified to define just what effect this media, or communications, revolution will produce. It is much too soon to be able to have any idea what sort of effect television will ultimately have on society. It took hundreds of years for people to figure out what print was doing to cultures. Television has been in general use for only about twenty-five years. Portable television has existed for only a few years. What we now see as the tremendous effects of television and other media, are probably only ripples that will be glossed over by future sociologists. We can in no way determine what the results of the Media Revolution will be. All we can hope to do is to become fully involved with all our senses primed and ready to react in a visually literate manner.

INTRODUCTION

Making The Media Revolution does not deal with a political revolution, but a revolution in communications. The media revolution is an everyday occurrence that affects all our lives more and more significantly as the electronic media become an all-encompassing phenomenon. It is the purpose of this book to make everyone aware of not only how to have some effect on the ways of this revolution, but to understand exactly what it is that is taking place, and to be able to work with the new media and take an active part in the revolution.

The book deals mainly with the techniques of portable electrography. The term "electrography" was first used on the old *Smothers Brothers* show. As video is now beginning to be recognized as an art form, let us use terminology that recognizes that fact. I define *electrography* as the art or process of producing images and sound, in perfect synchronization with one another, on magnetic (video) tape. It is understood that the video tape recorder, or "vtr," is the actual device that accomplishes this task, but the electrographer has complete control over the process, so that it is he, not the machine, that is responsible for the images transmitted to the tape.

The book begins with a simple, but thorough, discussion of how the television signal works. I don't believe it possible for you to use your equipment to its fullest capability, unless you understand just how it is doing what you are making it do.

Each chapter then describes one piece of equipment or technique that, hopefully, you will find valuable in your planned television programs. You can read the book in any order. The only reason for the order I have selected, is that it allows me to use terms throughout the book that can best be defined early in the book. Also, no one topic is fully discussed in any one chapter. Since there is so much interchangeability in television, information about different production elements runs through nearly every chapter.

I have used and tried all the equipment and techniques mentioned in this book. All of the information contained in the following chapters comes from my own experience with electrography. I have attempted to pass along to you what I have learned from this experience. There are shortcuts and money-saving hints included that I have found valuable. Also, I have tried to give an idea of how the networks accomplish some of the same things they do. I hope this will help you to better understand what you watch on broadcast television.

I have given prices where I feel they won't change drastically in the near future. Otherwise, I do not mention brand names unless the product is clearly superior, and has proven to be very valuable in actual production situations. You should keep in mind that technology is progressing at an extremely rapid rate, and the hardware available at this writing may be somewhat dated by the time you read this. Basic systems remain the same, however, and so do good techniques. I am sure that you will find the information given here to be of value for quite some time to come.

Learn from this book, but don't depend on it alone. I hope that you will use your imagination to develop new techniques, new concepts, and maybe even new equipment for the rest of us electographers to use.

It may seem incongruous to be learning about nonprint information retrieval and distribution from a book. However, at the present time, print is the most efficient and widely available communications medium we have. Hopefully, the day is not far off, when the electrographer's nonprint medium will be as efficient and as widely available as the writer's.

MAKING
THE MEDIA
REVOLUTION

CHAPTER 1

THE ELECTRONIC IMAGE

More and more people are becoming fascinated with the effects of television. Daily, new underground and establishment-type small-scale television productions are being made for enjoyment, educational purposes, and for sale to distributors. Electrographers are getting to be more familiar with their medium than ever before, and are asking this medium to do more for them than was ever expected by the engineers who originally designed the systems with which we work. The only way to get more out of a system than was originally designed into it is to have a full knowledge of the basics. In order to create the effects, moods, and images, described in the rest of the book, you need to know *why* a system works, as well as *how*.

This chapter deals with the television signal itself. It describes what happens to an image from the time you aim a camera at the subject to the time it is played back on a television screen. Hopefully, this information will allow you to adjust most television cameras, recorders, and monitors to achieve the best possible image.

Television is an extremely technical medium, and since this book is intended for production-oriented people and not engineers, great technical detail is avoided. A more detailed discussion is provided in Appendix D.

Since the most familiar thing about television to all of us is

1

the image on the screen, we will begin there. There are three types of devices through which a television signal can be played: a receiver, a video monitor, and a monitor/receiver. A *receiver* is the kind of television set you have at home. It receives its signal from a radio frequency (RF) picked up through its antenna. The receiver has a *tuner* which can select from a number of different frequencies (channels 2–13, VHF, and 14–83, UHF). An audio receiver and amplifier are inherent parts of a receiver.

A *video monitor* can only pick up a signal by a cable. The cable carries a video signal. It cannot receive a broadcast signal, and unless it is specially adapted, it cannot pick up or play back any audio. Monitors are used in studios or whenever the only information needed is the video signal. They are usually of a much higher quality and have better picture resolution than receivers, and they are used the check picture quality from cameras and other sources.

A *monitor/receiver* can be used either as a regular receiver

Video monitor. Courtesy Ampex Corp.

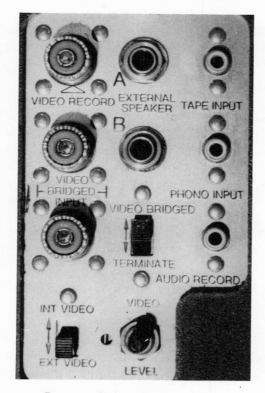

Rear panel of monitor/receiver.

or as a monitor. Many portable systems are supplied with them. You can record broadcast programs onto your video tape recorder from the set while it is in the receiver mode and then play the recorded program back in the monitor mode.

Once again, there are three basic kinds of television sets. The first is the *receiver*. This is the set you have at home that receives radio frequency, or *RF* signals, the kind of signals that are transmitted over the airwaves. Another way of watching a picture is over a *monitor*. The monitor can only accept a *video signal*. The video signal only travels over a cable, unlike the RF signal which can be broadcast. The third way is over a *monitor/receiver*, which can accept either a video signal or an RF signal, depending upon your need.

A video signal can be fed into a receiver only through an *RF adaptor*. RF adaptors are inexpensive and highly recommended.

3

Lines that make up television picture.

They convert an RF signal to a video signal on a particular channel, usually channel 3 or channel 4, depending on which channel is not being used in your area. Attach the adaptor to the antenna terminals of any receiver, and you have an instant monitor.

Television cameras create a video signal. If you look closely at a television screen, you will see that it is made up of numerous horizontal lines. The electronic information that comes into the set is made up of these lines, which are fed into an *electron gun* and sprayed across the screen from left to right, and from top to bottom. On the inside of the picture tube, there is a coating that glows when this spray hits it. How brightly the coating glows depends on the strength of the spray, or signal. If there is a dark portion of a scene, that portion of the signal is weak; if it is bright, the gun sprays a strong beam of electrons at that portion of the screen, to make it glow more brightly. The part of the picture tube that is hit by the gun's spray is called the *raster*. That portion of the raster that is visible to the viewer is called the *screen*.

Aside from the picture information that is being sent into the monitor, other information is being transmitted. These are known as *synchronizing pulses*. These *sync* pulses tell the electron gun when

4

to halt at the end of a line and when to move down to to the next line. The gun begins to spray on the left side of the screen, and moves across to the right. When a sync pulse comes along, the gun shuts down, and flips back to the left again, and once again picks up the picture signal and continues spraying. So, the bits of information that are constantly being supplied to the gun go picture-sync-picture-sync-picture-sync, etc.

The electron gun sprays the raster with 262½ lines of picture information. This is known as one *field*. At the end of a field, that is, on the last line of picture information, the gun receives a different type of sync signal which tells the gun to go back up to the top left-hand corner of the raster and begin spraying again. It takes the gun a sixtieth of a second to spray each field. Therefore, there are sixty fields per second. To create an illusion of motion, you must have at least forty separate pictures a second. At sixty fields per second, television has a very smooth flow of apparent motion.

Each field is only half a picture. The first field of any picture contains the odd-numbered lines, and the second contains the even-numbered ones. An important thing to look for when purchasing inexpensive video systems, is the type of sync used in the system. The best possible sync is *positive*, or *EIA, interlace* sync, in which the even lines fall exactly between the odd ones. Next best is *interlace* sync, in which the odd and even lines alternate, but are not centered with respect to one another. The cheapest and decidedly least desirable form of sync is *random interlace*, which is just what it says. Try to avoid random interlace if at all possible. (For a discussion of sync in slightly more detail, see Appendix D.)

Two interlaced fields compose one *frame*. Each frame contains the full 525 lines of the American system (two 262½ line fields). Since a frame is a complete picture, and it is made up of two fields, a new frame occurs every thirtieth of a second. The fact that there is a term *frame* does not mean that a frame actually exists on the video tape. There is nothing visible on the tape. Frames are clearly visible on motion picture film, and each frame of a movie is held stationary while it is being projected. Video frames on the other hand do not have to be moved into position, and held there, to be seen. They occur due to the retentive capability of the retina of the eye. The retina retains the image of the first field as the second field is being shown, and the image of this second field, as the first field of the next frame comes on the screen. It is the brain, not the video tape, that constructs two fields into one frame. If you take still pictures from a television screen, make sure you set your shutter speed at $\frac{1}{30}$ of a second or slower. Otherwise you will only pick up part of the total frame, not a complete picture, and your photograph will not be as sharp as the image on the television screen.

Another term that you will come in contact with when considering television equipment is *resolution*. Resolution describes the accuracy with which a television system reproduces the image of an actual object. Resolution is measured in *lines,* but these lines do not refer to the lines on the face of the picture screen. They refer to the lines on a test pattern. The lines of resolution are a numerical standard against which picture quality is measured.

When looking at a test pattern you will see two types of wedges made up of lines converging to a point. The lines in each wedge get narrower and closer together as they converge toward the point of the wedge. Alongside each wedge there are numbers that rise by hundreds (300, 400, 500) as the lines get thinner. When watching the image of these lines on a television screen, you will notice that at one spot the individual lines can no longer be distinguished. At this point all the lines seem to become one thick line, the number

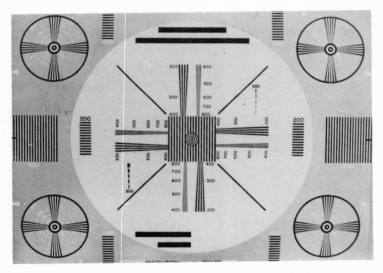

Test pattern—note horizontal and vertical wedges of lines for measuring resolution.

closest to this spot indicates the resolution of that piece of equipment.

Most portable television cameras are fully automatic in their "setup," or in the way in which they get ready to transmit an image. However, very few other kinds of television cameras are automatic, and a simple discussion of the controls that will confront you on most cameras will come in quite handy. To achieve a good conceptual understanding of the medium with which you are working, read Appendix D. The better you understand the complicated workings of this medium, the better your results will be, and the more you will be able to make television do for you. Even if your only exposure to video is with automatic Porta-Pak type equipment, it will be to your benefit to understand what makes up the signal leaving your camera.

The next four chapters will deal with the various formats, cameras, video tape recorders, and audio equipment that will confront you when working in electography. The first five chapters are designed to give you an understanding of how and why television equipment works, and how to make it work more efficiently for you. The remainder of the book will help you to use this information in preparing your productions by giving you information about helpful techniques to aid in presenting your material in the most pleasing and effective manner.

CHAPTER 2

WHICH FORMAT FOR YOU?

There are presently four different formats in television. The first is the *broadcast* format, which uses 2″ video tape, and video tape recorders (vtr's) having four heads, called *quad* machines. The second type of format is known as *institutional*. This refers to equipment that would be priced in the range of colleges and schools. Generally speaking, institutional equipment consists of vtr's that use 1″ or ½″ tape, and the machines are called *slant track*, or *helical scan*. The third format group is the *industrial* type. Industrial is a term that is used mostly in connection with surveillance cameras. These cameras and vtr's are usually of very poor quality and are the least expensive of all four types. The last and newest format is the *cassette*. Cassettes are helical scan in design, but some use ¾″ tape, so they do belong in their own category.

Broadcast television has certain technical requirements that have been established by the Federal Communications Commission (FCC). These standards were designed to insure that the broadcast signal would be the best possible signal attainable for the home receiver. It involves such things as very high-quality time-base stability, and superior sync. Because of the high technical standards required of broadcasters, their equipment is large and bulky, and it is also very good. However, they are limited because of the size and weight of their equipment, and consequently they do not have

1" and ½" video tape compared with Super 8mm film.

the portability and flexibility of the less expensive and slightly poorer quality of the other formats.

Basically, the difference in all the formats is most noticeable in the vtr's. Broadcast vtr's have four small heads that rotate at 14,400 rpm. They pass over the two-inch wide tape, which is moving at a speed of fifteen inches per second. This extremely high recording speed is responsible for the very high quality of the recording made on this type of machine. There are also numerous electronic superiorities built into the machines that make the signal that they emit a very high-quality one, one good enough to meet the tough FCC standards.

All of these factors contribute to the cost of the machine, however, and it is assumed that the reader of this book is not in the position to lay out the type of money needed to equip his facilities with broadcast quality recorders and cameras. Quad vtr's can cost upwards of $100,000, as can the cameras used in those studios. The quality is superb, but the cost and technical proficiency needed to operate this equipment make it unsuitable for the portable electrographer.

Industrial equipment uses slant track or helical scan vtr equip-

1" video tape recorder. Courtesy Ampex Corp.

ment. This type of gear is of a very low quality, since the people using it are not concerned with the quality and esthetic beauty of the signal produced. The inexpensive equipment in this category is used in banks, warehouses, stockrooms, parking lots, etc., or anywhere that theft is likely to occur. The cameras are usually tied in to a burglar alarm system, or to a console where a guard can sit and monitor the activity in different areas of a building, or complex of buildings and outdoor areas. The cameras don't need to have very high resolution because minute details are not needed. All that has to be detected are movements and general features.

There are some highly expensive cameras in this field, however. These are known as *low-light level* cameras. Whereas a normal camera needs at least 20 foot candles to pick up any kind of picture, these special cameras can produce surprisingly clear images with light levels as low as 10^{-7} foot candles. If you know anything about math, 10^{-7} is an infinitesimally small number, so small that that is

10

½" video tape recorder.

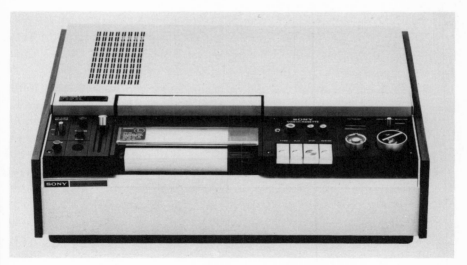

¾" video cassette recorder. Courtesy Sony Corp.

less light than the human eye needs to see. I have seen demonstrations of this equipment in what apparently were absolutely dark rooms. Tapes have been made there with these cameras, and when played back, the faces of the individuals in the room were completely recognizable on the tape, even though you literally could not see the person sitting next to you.

The low-light level cameras are the exception to the rule for industrial quality machines, however. For the most part, they are very cheap and of relatively poor quality. Some of these items should not be overlooked by the electrographer, though, since the price is right, and this equipment can fulfill some requirements that you may have.

The class of equipment most suited to our needs is the institutional variety. Until recently this format was used exclusively for instructional programs, for training and enrichment in schools and business. The equipment is still basically designed for this type of user in general, but the moderate price and the good quality of the machines lends itself to the electrographer's needs very well. Cassettes also fit into this sphere, so this part of the discussion will concern them as well.

Briefly, helical scan recording refers to the manner in which the information is put on tape, not the size of the tape itself. Quad machines use only two-inch tape. Helical scan machines are available for two inch, one inch, half inch, quarter inch, vtr's, and cassettes in ½" and ¾" varieties. The quality varies greatly between different helical scan machines, and the size of the tape has little to do with the performance or the quality of the signal produced.

The two-inch format in helical scan is being phased out, and these machines are becoming fairly hard to obtain, as are spare

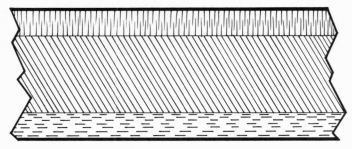

Manner in which information is put down on helical-scan video tape.

parts. For this reason the only thing to be said about them is to stay away from two-inch helical scan. It will be too expensive in the long run and the state of the art in video has long since passed them by.

The term *helical scan* refers to the way the information is placed on the tape. The video information is layed down in a diagonal to the direction of the tape movement. The path which the tape follows in its movement around the video head, or heads, is slanted upward. Some slant track machines have one video head, usually the 1″ machines, and others have two heads, most often the ½″, and ¼″ tapes, and ¾″ cassettes.

Technology has made great advances in the design of helical scan equipment. Today the state of the art is moving the fastest in ½″ equipment, but 1″ is still way ahead in picture quality. One-inch recorders have excellent picture quality and stability. They have high picture resolution, and some of the expensive models (here we talk in terms of $20,000, or one-fifth the price of quad machines) are capable of producing a signal superior enough to meet the FCC requirements. Indeed, some small television stations are using these high-quality one-inch helical scan machines to broadcast with.

The major drawback to 1″ is that there is no one industrywide format for how the information is placed on the tape. In other words, a tape made on an Ampex vtr will not play back on an IVC vtr. There is no *compatibility* in one-inch recorders. *Compatibility* is a term used to define how well a tape recorded on one machine will play back on another. In the not too distant past, even tapes made on one model of a particular brand would not play back on another model of the same manufacturer. They were not compatible. Now all manufacturers insist that all the vtr's in their product line be compatible, a tape made on the cheapest machine will play back on the best machine in their line, and vice versa.

On ½″ vtr's the problem was solved much sooner. All the manufacturers had decided on one format for black and white. This was called the *EIAJ* (Electronic Industries Association-Japan) format. Because the manufacturers all got together, on ½″ recording you can play back a tape recorded on any EIAJ machine that was recorded on any other EIAJ vtr. This means that a Sony tape will play back on a Panasonic tape deck. More recently a standard was set for color, so now both color and black-and-white tapes are completely compatible on all ½″ vtr's that use the EIAJ formats. Make sure, however, that the machine you purchase is compatible both in color and black and white. There are still a number of EIAJ type machines around that are compatible only in black and white. Take the time to make the extra check about color, since this total compatibility is well worth your effort.

The cassette manufacturers have not as yet decided on an industrywide format for their machines, but they do use the helical scan format. It would be well worth your while to wait to see if one format is going to appear in casettes before you invest in them. If you do go ahead and buy some cassette equipment, and the model you buy is not the one chosen by the Electronic Industries Association (EIA) for the industry standard, you will own obsolete equipment. Needless to say, that is not something you should let happen to you easily.

Of the four formats discussed, three fall into the helical scan category. Broadcast equipment, the quad vtr's, are not what this book is about. We deal exclusively with the applications of the helical scan format. Nearly all the techniques discussed can be and are being used in broadcast television. However, they take on a different form when being related to on a "portable" level. With the exception of the big expensive one-inch vtr's, all helical scan equipment is portable to the extent that it does not have to remain in one spot to operate at peak efficiency. Any small-scale television production, no matter how sophisticated and complex it may be, can be handled with slant track equipment. Both studio and portable helical scan equipment is now receiving the benefits of very advanced technology. Companies are pouring great amounts of money into research and design of better portable gear. What was unavailable in the helical scan market a few years ago, for any price, is easily attainable today. For example, two years ago even the most expensive ½″ vtr's did not offer electronic editing of the tape as a feature. Now you can get a machine that not only records and plays back in black and white and color (color is not an inherent feature of television; it must be added on or built in as an extra), but also offers electronic editing that is just as good as the very expensive 1″ vtr's, for a price under $1,500 ($\frac{1}{100}$ the price of a broadcast vtr). The appeal of ½″ vtr's should become apparent at this point.

14

Which Format for You?

The type of equipment that is available to you (as an individual, a school, or an independent production team, planning on developing electrography to its fullest extent) is neither terribly expensive nor unsophisticated. This discussion has, hopefully, pointed out some of the differences in the various types of equipment, and what you might expect from machines using different sizes of tape. The width of the tape that is used on a particular vtr can be a guide to the type of machine it is, as well as to the features that can be expected from it and to the price. The wider the tape, the more expensive the machine, and the more expensive the tape itself. Presently, the wholesale price of one-inch video tape is under $40 for a one-hour tape. You should be able to purchase ½″ tape for under $30 an hour, and ¼″ tape is about $7 for twenty minutes. The price of the medium itself should be an important determining factor in your choice of format.

If you can afford it, one-inch equipment has the highest quality. Half-inch comes in as a close second in quality, and is considerably cheaper. Quarter-inch is the cheapest, but very little is available in this tape size, and until more is done with it, it is recommended that you avoid this format. Cassettes will be priced similarly to half-inch tape, depending upon length. The quality of cassette recorders can be expected to be very high, with ¾″ being at least as good as present 1″ gear. The best complement of equipment is one that uses the best of all formats. Half-inch portable units, the Porta-Paks, can be used for recording programs in the field, and they can then be dubbed to one-inch vtr's for editing and duplication. Use the various formats for what they are best at, since mixing formats will pay off only if you use each for its best qualities.

CHAPTER 3

FEATURES OF VIDEO CAMERAS

The single most important piece of equipment you will ever buy is your camera. Virtually everything you do in planning and setting up a production will revolve around your camera and its capabilities. How well you get to know your camera will determine what your final tapes will look like. The more you use it, the more you will understand its peculiarities and quirks, and the better your camera-work will become.

This chapter will discuss the different types of television cameras available, their advantages and disadvantages, and will explain some of the differences between various camera systems.

Basically there are three kinds of television cameras. They are broken down into categories by the type of pickup tube they use. The first is called *Image Orthicon,* or *I-O*. There are I-O tubes that are 3 or 4½ inches in diameter. The advantage of the larger tube is the same as the advantage one has in photography when using a larger film format. You get a much sharper enlargement from a 2¼″ x 2¼″ negative than you do from a 35mm negative, simply because you have more picture area to work with. The same holds true in video. The larger the faceplate of the pick-up tube, the better the quality of the resulting picture will be. Consequently, most broadcasters use the 4½″ I-O tube in their cameras. This is a very high-quality tube which produces the images that you are used to seeing

16

on your home receiver. It produces an image of much higher resolution than any home receiver is capable of showing.

The I-O camera is quite expensive and is used mainly by broadcasters and colleges. The colleges most often use I-O cameras that have been donated to them by television stations. These are really the only people who can run I-O gear because this type of equipment needs a considerable amount of technical know-how to be serviced, and it needs constant attention if it is to be run at full efficiency.

There are certain characteristics of I-O cameras that bear some discussion. The Image Orthicon tube needs from 50 to 100 foot candles of light to produce a good image. This is quite low when compared to other kinds of cameras. A foot candle is a method of measuring light for photographic purposes. The average fluorescent lit school classroom has between 20 to 30 foot candles of light. Thus, this type of camera requires very little extra lighting.

The I-O tube is very sensitive to *burn-in.* As the tube gets older, it becomes more and more sensitive to burning. When we say an image is "burned-in" to the faceplate of a camera, we mean that the image is extremely bright or contrasty, and that the tube will retain a negative of that image long after the camera has stopped looking at that image. Understandably, this is highly undesirable.

I-O tubes have relatively short life spans, usually under 1,000 hours. For this reason, they age quickly, and are soon susceptible to burns. Many I-O cameras have a device known as an *orbiter,* which moves the image slowly about the surface of the faceplate, to keep any image from remaining in one spot long enough to create a burn. Tubes with a nonburnable surface are available, and they are fairly reliable. Remedies for burn-ins are discussed in Chapter 7 on lighting.

Because of the large size and heavy weight of the cameras that use I-O tubes and because of the fabulous expense of this type of equipment, they don't make any sense in terms of portable electrography. Broadcasters use this expensive and highly technical device for only one reason: its high picture quality. They can afford the initial expense and upkeep required, and the engineering staff that comes along with the equipment. Replacing just the I-O tubes in a three-tube color camera can buy a ½" vtr. And remember, those tubes have a short life span!

The next major type of pickup tube is known as the *Plumbicon.* Plumbicon is the trademark name of a tube invented by the Dutch company, Philips. This company took the versatile vidicon tube, and applied a different type of surface to the faceplate. Plumbicons are mainly used in color cameras, but there are numerous black-and-white applications available. There are some excellent characteristics inherent to the Plumbicon tube. The first of these is its low-light level requirements. It needs around 75 foot candles for good pictures, and newer Plumbicons are producing high-quality color pictures at under 20 foot candles. Also, there is very little chance of burn-in, since these tubes are very insensitive to this problem. Plumbicons also have a very good contrast range, which means that extremes between very bright and dark elements in a picture can be well represented.

There are some drawbacks, however, but these are being ironed out and should be no detriment after a while. Plumbicons do have the capacity to show lag in the picture, but not severely. Also, the picture resolution is not as high as it could be, but better than vidicon. Color Plumbicon tubes have some trouble in picking up reds; however, the addition of silicon diodes eliminates this problem.

All in all, Plumbicons are reliable, high-quality pickup tubes. They are not nearly as expensive as I-O tubes, and they are considerably lighter, therefore, more portable. They are, generally speaking, a good investment if you can afford it. The only problem is that they are not appearing as standard equipment in the Porta-Pak type format. Some manufacturers are going so far as to make their cameras upgradable to Plumbicon from vidicon, however, and this should be an important factor in your decision.

The *vidicon* tube has by far the greatest number of applications of the three tubes discussed. There are so many advantages to the vidicon that they far outweigh the shortcomings. For our purposes, the greatest advantage of the vidicon is its size. Where the best I-O tube has a diameter of 4½″, good-quality pictures can be obtained from a ⅔″ vidicon tube. This makes the size and weight of the cameras considerably smaller than either of the other two types. Also, the life expectancy of a vidicon tube is much longer than that of an I-O, and its initial cost is a fraction of the others.

Some disadvantages are that many vidicons need a considerable amount of light to operate effectively. At least 100 foot candles are required for most studio-type vidicons, and 200 foot candles will produce better results. Porta-Pak equipment will, however, produce

18

Vidicon tube.

good-quality pictures at around 20 foot candles. Lag is an unfortunate feature of vidicons, since they are particularly susceptible to it. The only remedies are to not move the camera quickly away from an object, and to avoid very low-light level situations, since this is where lag is most likely to occur.

Vidicons are quite insensitive to burns, and this is why they are used at television stations to show title cards and other graphics. This is a handy feature, and one that is vital to a one-camera setup. If you have only one camera, and that camera has a bad burn in it, you either have to suspend operation until the burn is gone, or use the camera with the burn showing, which is highly undesirable. If you have a camera that is relatively safe from burns, you don't have to worry much about this problem. You should, however, take extreme care to keep any camera away from potential burning situations.

Because of its low cost, light weight, ease of operation, and availability, the vidicon is the most popular camera in the electographer's options of equipment. Broadcast television's reluctance to use vidicon equipment is based primarily upon its supposed poor-picture quality. This is a myth. There are vidicon tubes available at a higher cost that will produce 1,000 lines of picture resolution. When you consider that the average home receiver can offer only about 250 lines of resolution, it can be seen that these tubes can produce pictures far superior to anything that can be seen on the home screen. I-O tubes do produce better-quality pictures, and these are needed for the transmission of the video signal over the air waves, but for our purposes, the vidicon tube produces a more than acceptable image.

There are two basic types of vidicon camera: the *viewfinder* and the *nonviewfinder*. The viewfinder camera is so called because it has a monitor built on or attached to it that enables the cameraman to see exactly what he is shooting. Studio vidicon cameras have view-

Viewfinder vidicon camera.

finder screens that can be from three to six inches across. The Porta-Pak type units generally use one-inch screens for their view-finders.

Nonviewfinder cameras, obviously, have no monitors attached. They are usually at least $200 cheaper than cameras with view-finders. These cameras are used primarily for surveillance, and for

Nonviewfinder vidicon camera.

situations in a studio where no cameraman is required, such as for graphics or other fixed shots. Many nonviewfinder cameras have what is known as *optical viewfinders*. Optical viewfinders consist of a small lens that goes through the camera so that a cameraman can see what he is aiming at. Even though this is not precisely what the camera is seeing, it does allow him to align the camera in the general direction of the subject. As opposed to cameras with optical viewfinders, cameras with built-in monitors are sometimes referred to as *electronic viewfinder* cameras. Most nonviewfinder cameras are exactly the same as other cameras in a manufacturer's line, but without the monitors built on. Many of these have the capability of being upgraded to viewfinder status by simple attachment of a monitor and some cables. This is an important thing to look for, because if you can't afford a viewfinder on one of your cameras right away, it will be handy to be able to add one on at some future date when you can better afford to do so.

Camera cables come in different configurations, depending upon your needs. The simplest cable will have only video and power cords. For the sake of clarity, a camera cable is referred to as "a cable" no matter how many different cables are actually involved. The two cords above, for example, power and video, make up one cable. As the camera becomes more sophisticated, other functions are added that can include power, video, sync, intercom, playback, line, tally light, and the remote control functions of such things as beam, target, and electronic focus. Even if the camera you buy has only a power cord and a video cable as standard features, you should get the optional cable that will include all the functions you might ever need. This will make upgrading your system much easier at a later date.

Many new manufacturers are putting out video equipment every day, and the state of the art is constantly changing. Cameras, as well as all other television equipment, are constantly being improved. An interesting thing to note is that as the equipment gets better, it also seems to get less expensive. This is one case where the consumer always wins; as the quality goes up, the price goes down. Let us hope that this unique situation continues.

Another interesting thing about the manufacturers is that they really seem to be responsive to the users' needs. They have shown much willingness to provide new equipment just as needs arise. The technology is moving along at just about the same rate as the art.

21

CHAPTER 4

THE VIDEO TAPE RECORDER

The determining factor of quality of any video system is the video tape recorder. You may have a camera capable of a thousand lines of resolution, but if the vtr it is feeding will resolve only 300 lines, then that is all you get. Unless you do all your programming live, the vtr is the heart of your system. You must always treat it with care, give it constant attention, and above all, make sure that it is clean. Many excellent programs have been lost because no one checked to see if the video heads were clean. One of the most frustrating experiences in television is to complete a program that you felt was superb, only to be disappointed upon playback, by seeing that nothing was recorded. Proper care for your vtr will insure good, clean recordings.

We shall discuss simple maintenance in this chapter, as well as a brief explanation of how vtr's work, and the controls that are similar to all machines. Most vtr's are quite easy to operate, and becoming familiar with these controls should help you to quickly master the operating technique of just about any machine you might come across.

The purposes of this book are not to introduce you to the workings of broadcast equipment, but to equipment that is relatively portable. For this reason, we will not go into any explanation of the four-head, quadraplex vtr's that are used in broadcasting. Our discussion will be involved only with helical scan equipment. There are four kinds of helical scan: one-inch, quarter-inch, half-inch, reel-to-reel and cassette, and the three-quarter inch cassette format. All of the above formats are similar in the general way in which they put the electronic information onto the tape. They vary in the specific means and threading patterns that they use.

As has been discussed, there is absolutely no standardization in the one-inch format. A tape recorded on a machine produced by one manufacturer will not play back on a machine produced by any other manufacturer. There is no interchangeability. The same holds true for quarter-inch vtr's. Most manufacturers seem to be getting together on a single format for three-quarter inch and half-inch cassettes. However, this remains to be officially resolved. The only format where there is complete standardization is in the half-inch format. All companies have agreed to make their machines compatible with the Japanese EIAJ#1 black-and-white format, and the recommended EIAJ color format. This means that you are no longer required to buy only the machines produced by a single company. You can mix your system by using the best vtr available for a specific job, and be assured that any tape will play back on any other machine using the EIAJ formats. This is very important because before this agreement was reached, you had to stick with one particular manufacturer. You may have liked their editing machine, but possibly someone else's playback-only vtr was better and cheaper than the one in the format you were using. Now you can mix to your own satisfaction, using the best vtr from any company, with no worries of introducing a new format to your operation.

Other than format, there are other categories that vtr's fall into. These bear no relation to the tape size or manufacturer, but just to function, and they are common to all types of vtr's. The most basic machine of all is the *video tape player*. The player has no record capability, and will play back only pre-recorded tapes. Players are the least expensive of all machines and are used in applications where no recording will ever take place, for example, in classrooms, where the possibility of accidental erasure exists, and in remote corporation locations, where training tapes are sent from the main office. If you anticipate having a situation where a playback-only situation will exist, considerable money can be saved by purchasing a video tape player.

Making the Media Revolution

Similar to the player is the video tape recorder that has no playback function. This *record-only vtr* is found only in portable systems. The reason for this is that the Porta-Pak systems try to save weight wherever possible. The rewind motors and playback electronics definitely add weight to the vtr, and since the Porta-Pak was originally conceived to be just a remote camera and recorder, it was assumed that the tape would be brought back to an operations type area, where the tape could be rewound and played back on a table model vtr. If this sounds like an inconvenience to you, make sure to check out the system you plan on buying to make sure it has a playback mode. Porta-Paks without playback are lighter and cheaper than those with it. You must decide what is best for your application.

The simple black-and-white *video tape recorder/player* is the basic model. It has no features other than the ability to record and play back picture and sound. An important aspect to look for when purchasing equipment is whether the basic machine is upgradable, that is, whether it can be made more sophisticated by adding an electronics package. If you want a machine that will only record and play back black-and-white programs, you don't have to spend the extra money to get a machine that offers you the possibility of more sophistication. If, on the other hand, you feel you may want to up-

Mechanical edit function.

grade your equipment at a later date, see if the machine you want has this feature.

Vtr's that can be upgradable start with a basic black-and-white package. Most can already record programs in color, but they can't play them back. You can add a circuit board that will give you a color playback function. This generally costs about $500. Most of the features we will discuss from here on can be added to upgradable vtr's.

Editing decks come in various degrees of sophistication. All editors are described in greater detail in Chapter 15 on editing, but for our purposes here a brief description will be given. The simplest kind of *editing deck* offers a mechanical edit. All this does is allow you to go from a playback function to the record mode without stopping the machine. Mechanical edits are the simplest form of editing that a vtr can offer, but they cannot be considered an electronic function of the machine, and the quality is not the best.

Electronic editors are the most sophisticated method of editing video tape and the most reliable. They also add more to the price of the vtr. There are two kinds of electronic edits. The simpler of the two is called an *assemble* edit. This kind of editor allows you to add information to the end of a segment of tape, without producing any

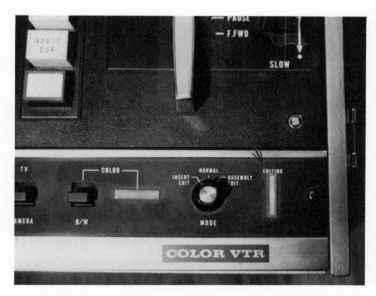

Electronic edit function.

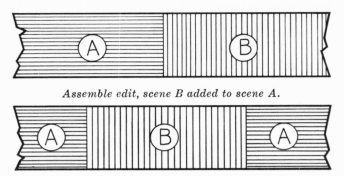

Assemble edit, scene B added to scene A.

Insert edit, scene B inserted within scene A.

defects on the picture when it is introduced to the tape. The second and more sophisticated is known as an *insert* editor. The insert device allows you to insert material into an already existing segment, without disturbing the beginning and end of that material. You can also do assemble editing with an insert editor.

On all helical scan vtr's, with the exception of some cassettes, one reel is higher above the surface of the machine than the other. On one-inch machines, the take-up reel is generally the higher one; on EIAJ half-inch machines, it is the supply reel that is the higher of the two. The tape moves through the head assembly from left to right. The head assembly is level with the deck of the vtr, so the tape moves across it diagonally on its passage from the reel at one level to the reel on the other level. In other words, half-inch tapes move laterally down across the heads. This is the reason they are called *helical scan* or *slant track* video tape recorders.

All helical scan vtr's have from five to seven heads in the head assembly. A *head* is a tiny electromagnet that has a gap between its poles. When recording, the audio, video, and sync signals are fed into the respective heads, which creates a varying magnetic field. The video tape that passes the heads by is also magnetic (it is sometimes referred to as "magnetic" tape), and this varying field is recorded onto the tape. Upon playback, the heads pick up these fields, and convert them into electronic signals that are the same as those originally recorded. This signal is then fed into the monitor to reproduce the information as it was first scanned by the electron gun in the camera. The heads which the video tape passes on its journey through the machine are the one or two video heads; one or

26

Supply reel higher than takeup reel on ½" EIAJ standard vtr.

two audio heads, depending on how many audio tracks the machine offers; the control track head, which lays down the sync track; the video erase head, used during recording and editing, to insure that the new signal has an electronically clean area on the tape to magnetize; and the audio erase head, similar to the video erase head, in that it eliminates any previous audio information during recording and editing.

The recording surface of video tape has an oxide formula impregnated onto it. It is this oxide onto which the heads pass their information. After a few recordings or playbacks you will notice a residue on the heads themselves. This buildup of oxide is unavoidable, and will result in poor picture quality and stability, or no picture

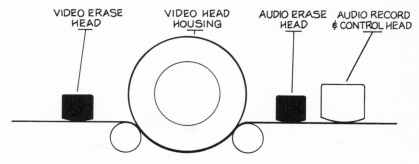

Head assembly on ½" vtr.

27

at all. For the best possible results, clean the video heads before each use of the machine. The audio and control heads need be cleaned only once daily, unless the vtr is being used a great deal.

The frequency of cleaning depends on a number of factors. The first is the tape that you are using. Only use video tape on your machine that has been specifically formulated for your make and model of vtr. The manner in which the oxide particles are placed on the tape is determined by the method the vtr uses to put the information onto the tape. Different models do this differently, with the exception of the EIAJ machines. When purchasing tape, be sure to tell the salesman exactly what kind of machine you will be using the tape on. All video tape manufacturers make tape for virtually every vtr made. The use of the wrong tape will cause head clogging and wear, as well as producing poor picture quality.

Also, no matter how reliable and well known the manufacturer, they *can* supply you with defective tape. This has happened to the largest tape manufacturers, and they usually will make good on any bad tape you may have. A bad run of tape can be recognized by instant head clogging, and sometimes, even the ruining of video heads. Some manufacturers will replace heads that were damaged by their tape, but you have to keep after them. If the heads clog too often on your vtr, stop using the tape! If you can see residue building up on the heads, use some other brand of tape, and call the salesman who sold you this tape. Also, call other people you know who might have purchased the same tape at around the same time as you. If they are also having problems, the manufacturer will be more willing to exchange tapes with you. If you should be an isolated case, you will have less negotiating strength. After having trouble several times with bad tape runs, many people have taken to ordering their raw stock in smaller quantities. When purchasing in large lots, you may get a discount, but if you have bought a large lot of bad tape, it is just an additional hassle to get it exchanged. You may have to pay slightly more for smaller quantities of new tape, but you will be much safer in the long run.

ONLY USE VIDEO TAPE ON YOUR VTR! This bears repeating: ONLY USE VIDEO TAPE ON YOUR VTR! Some people use computer tape on their machines because it is so cheap. This is false economy. Video head manufacturers can tell you that they supply many new sets of heads to people who are after bargains in video tape. Computer tape is extremely inexpensive, but it produces poor picture quality, and tremendous head wear. Stay away from it. Video tape is the essence of this medium, and only quality products should be used. Read the trade journals to see the comparative tests that have been made. Keep abreast of new developments in manufacturing, and make comparisons yourself. Most reliable salesmen will be willing to leave a sample of their tape with you for a few days. Collect a number of samples and test them yourself. Everyone has individual standards against which he tests tape, and different things he looks for in a recording made with different tapes. A good test to make is to record the same information onto a number of different brands of tape. Mark the tapes and have someone splice them together in a random order. Watch the playback of this composite tape, and mark down the qualities of each segment as you watch. The one that seems consistently best to you is the one you should buy. Video tapes are different, and you should select the one that fits your needs the best.

Another factor that contributes to the amount of head cleaning that should take place is the general cleanliness of the room in which the vtr is stored. Vtr's are very sensitive machines, and they should be kept scrupulously clean, as should their surroundings. The more dirt in the air, the more often they will have to be cleaned.

When playing tapes back, you will occasionally see horizontal

Dropout.

black streaks go across the screen. These streaks are called *dropout*. Dropout occurs when a speck of dust or other dirt has covered or ruined a portion of the signal on the tape. Also, as the oxide on the tape wears off, information is lost. Some tapes are more susceptible to dropout than others, and this is something you should look for when buying video tape. A few vtr's can be purchased that come with *dropout compensators*. A dropout compensator senses the missing information, and will reinsert the information from the line that just preceded the missing line. This is an important feature to look for if you plan on doing much dubbing or editing. If a dropout occurs on a master tape, every copy will show that dropout, and add more of its own naturally. The fewer dropouts on the master tape, the fewer on the copies. In making copies with no regard to this problem, the number of dropouts per minute can snowball dramatically and cause very poor picture quality in subsequent showings.

Do not think that all these features will add greatly to the cost of a vtr. Technology is moving so fast that Panasonic has introduced an EIAJ half-inch machine that comes with black-and-white and color record and playback capability, an electronic insert and assemble editor, a dropout compensator, and stop action and slow motion modes, all as standard equipment. The total price for this package is only about $1,600.

A guide for the proper storage and handling of video tape is included in Appendix C of this book. Please refer to it, and follow the suggestions it makes. They will help to preserve your tapes for the maximum life span that can be expected.

The proper method for cleaning the heads of your particular vtr

Video head cleaner supplied by manufacturer.

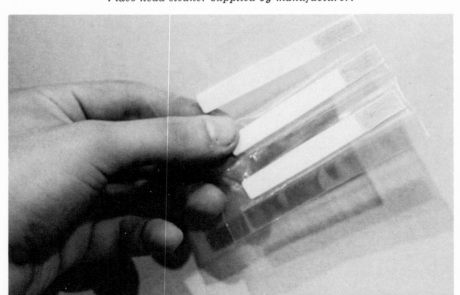

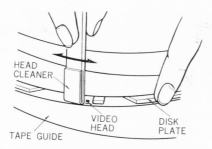

Head cleaning. Courtesy Panasonic Corp.

will be explained in detail in the instruction manual that came with the machine. However, there are a number of generally recommended ways of getting the video heads thoroughly clean. Some manufacturers supply a small bottle of head-cleaning solution with the machine when it is purchased. They will also supply some head-cleaning devices. These are broad, flat pieces of plastic about three inches long, with cotton on one end. Wet the cotton with the solution and very gently rub the heads in a horizontal motion. Always move the tip across the head from side to side. NEVER clean the heads with an up-and-down motion! This will cause undue damage to the head and possibly even ruin it. If your machine has two heads,

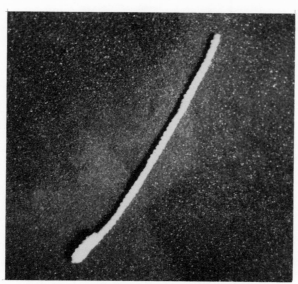

Pipe cleaner bent at tip for use as video head cleaner.

make sure that you do both. If you miss one head, you will see a strange image on the screen. The picture will look extremely snowy, with the image barely able to be seen through the snow.

If you don't get a head cleaner with the vtr you buy, or you have used up the fluid and the cleaners, you don't have to buy new ones from the manufacturer. You can use Freon or cleaning alcohol for the fluid, while pipe cleaners work very well as head-cleaning devices. Impregnate the pipe cleaners with either the Freon or the alcohol, and clean the heads in the same manner as described above.

The operating procedures of all vtr's are basically the same. The general rules listed below can be followed on all models. However, before attempting to operate any machine that is new to you, read the instruction manual carefully. You may think you can operate a machine, but you might find in the operating instruction manual some useful information on how to use the machine at its optimum level that you did not even know about.

When threading the vtr with tape, always be sure that the machine is turned off! Some machines allow you to stop the heads

On/off volume switch and tape counter.

Input selector switch.

from rotating while threading, but just to make sure, do not turn the machine on until the tape is fully threaded. If the heads are rotating during the threading process, they may be caught on a tape end and permanent damage could occur. Also, the tape might get caught up on the heads and pulled into the machine causing extensive damage.

When the tape is threaded properly, and checked, you can turn the machine on. The *on/off switch* usually also functions as the volume control on playback.

Once the machine is on, set the *tape counter*. All vtr's have some sort of marking systems. Some indicate the elapsed time; others use an arbitrary number system. There is no standardization in the various counter systems, and this would be a very handy thing to have indeed. None of the counters is very accurate, so if yours uses time to mark off taped segments, don't use the counter as a timer, but just as a guide. Use a stopwatch instead.

If you are going to be recording, the next step is to make sure that the *input selector switch* is in the proper position. Usually, you can choose between a signal coming from a camera or switcher, or from an off-air receiver.

Next, you must set your *audio* and *video* levels. If your machine has automatic gain control, AGC, this is unnecessary. If not, you must manually set the levels. The audio level is set in conjunction with a meter that will be visible usually near the level control knob. This meter is called a *volume unit,* or *VU* meter. The VU meter is discussed in Chapter 5 on audio. But for level-setting purposes, just make sure that the needle on the meter's face remains within

VU meter.

the acceptable zone, and does not often go into the red area. The *video gain control* will also have a meter nearby. If not, you must set the level by eye, by looking at a monitor, and setting the control where the picture looks the best. The needle on the video level meter should not fluctuate as it will on the audio meter. It should remain around one spot for the entire recording. The best place to set this control is to have the needle point to a spot between 95% and 100%, or just below the red area. When the meter reads "100%," the vtr is accepting one full volt of picture information.

On the rear of most vtr's you will find a number of input and

Video level meter.

output plugs and jacks. A brief description of the most common of these follows.

AC-in is the point where the power cord should be attached, if it is not permanently mounted on the machine. *AC-out* will feed any other equipment nearby, most often, a monitor. AC-out is handy, as it enables you to use fewer wall sockets.

Video-in is where the video signal is fed into the machine. This is also where the sync signal enters, unless other provisions are made for the sync. *Video-out* should be a one-volt composite signal that will allow you to show the tape on a monitor, or feed another recorder.

Audio-in is used for either the microphone input or any "line" audio: phonographs, audio tapes, or the audio from other video tapes. *Audio-out* or *line-out* will feed all the audio coming into the machine to another source. Some vtr's have a *mic-in* plug only. This will allow you to feed a microphone directly into the machine. If this is the case, and you want to feed more than one mike, or mix a tape and a mike, you will have to use an external audio mixer, and feed the mixer into this plug. Some machines have two audio-in and -out receptacles. In this case, you can mix the audio signals right at the vtr, by adjusting the audio levels. With two audio channels you can record in stereo if you desire.

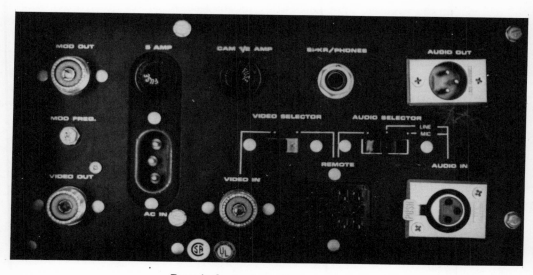

Rear jack panel on vtr.

Modulators for channels 3, 6, and 8.

Sync-in will allow you to add a different sync to the picture than is being supplied by the camera or vtr. This is very handy in editing, when you will want to use the best possible sync available. You can feed a sync generator into the vtr through this plug.

RF-out will supply a modulated signal for play back into a conventional television set. A regular receiver cannot be used to play back directly a program from a vtr, since it can only accept signals of certain frequencies (channels), and the audio and video must be mixed together, not separately as they come out of the vtr. A signal that has both audio and video information mixed together, that operates at a specific frequency, is called a *modulated*, or an *RF*, signal. A modulator is a device that takes the separate audio and video signals and mixes them to produce an RF signal. Some vtr's have RF converters (small modulators) built in. Others have the facility available at extra cost. Whatever the case may be, RF-out will feed any television set.

It is hoped that this chapter has given you an overview of the various formats and features available on video tape recorders. Also, the most common controls that will face you were explained to aid in familiarizing you with the operating procedures inherent on most machines.

If your vtr purchase was carefully thought out first in terms of price, features, and function, and if you take good care of it, you will find the video tape recorder to be one of the most versatile pieces of equipment you have ever owned.

CHAPTER 5

AUDIO

Many people become so involved with picture quality, and with special video effects, that they forget a production element that can make or break a program. Many a good visual program failed because the audio portion was sloppily put together. Indeed, we even call our medium "video." There is constant discussion going on as to the most important portion of a program. Is it the video or the audio? This is hard to determine, but it is safe to assume that depending upon the nature of the program, the audio accounts for at least 50 percent of the content of any program. With all the attention given to video, audio is all too often neglected, and the resulting program is severely lacking in quality. You must realize how vital good audio is to the success of any television program. Considerable time should be spent in familiarizing yourself with good audio techniques, and how to make the best of the equipment you have on hand. This chapter will discuss different types of microphones and other audio accessories, and some suggestions on how to make use of them.

Good audio is very hard to achieve in most television applications, because for the best possible sound reproduction, the source of the sound must be as close as possible to the microphone. As the distance increases, so does the possibility of extraneous noises being included in the recording. In most television situations, it is difficult to get the mike right in on the action. This is especially true if you are using a Porta-Pak, and you are a one-man operation. The mike built

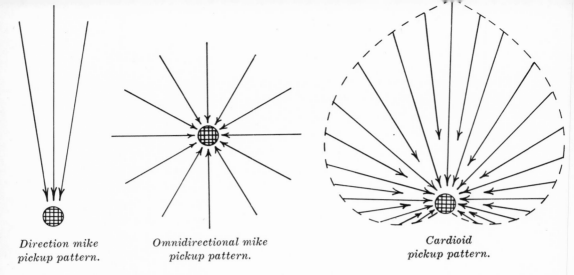

*Direction mike
pickup pattern.*

*Omnidirectional mike
pickup pattern.*

*Cardioid
pickup pattern.*

into most Porta-Paks is not the best possible recording device, and it will record sound coming into it from all directions. This is the first category of microphones: *the pick-up pattern.*

The pick-up patterns of all microphones fall into two major categories: *directional* and *omni-* or *non-directional*. The *omni-directional* mike, like the kind built into the Porta-Pak systems, will receive sound from any direction. This is quite handy when recording groups of people, and when recording background sound to be added to another tape at a later date. The drawback to nondirectional mikes is that they let in all the unwanted noise of the recording location. That is, you hear the air conditioner, the telephone, footsteps, coughing, etc. For this reason, omnidirectional mikes should be used only in the situations that call for an instrument that has the specific qualities of this type microphone.

Unlike the human ear, microphones hear everything. The difference between our ears and mikes is that we have a brain that allows us to listen selectively. When in a crowded room, we can talk to a friend, and really only listen to what he has to say, without allowing the other room noise to interfere. The brain receives all the sound coming in through the ear, but disregards all the noise that does not pertain to the conversation we are having with our friend.

Microphones, unfortunately, do not have this capability. They hear and transmit for recording all the sound that they can pick up. For example, when playing back a recording of a conversation in a crowded room, we are subjected to all the noise in that situation, without any discrimination as to the most important elements of the conversation itself.

38

For the above reason, *directional* microphones were developed. They do not provide the discrimination of the human brain, but they will not pick up sound that does not approach the mike from a predetermined direction. Most directional mikes have a *cardioid* pick-up pattern. In other words, the directions from which sound can come to be picked up by the mike is a heart-shaped pattern, with the point of the heart facing front. Virtually nothing behind the mike, and only something of the sound to either side of the mike, will be received. However, sound coming in from the front of the mike, in whatever direction it is pointed, will be received most strongly. The best application for a mike with a cardioid pattern would be in front of a noisy room, where you would like to pick up the sound from the speakers in the front, but not too much of the audience noise.

There are numerous types of directional mikes, ranging from the cardioid to the *shotgun mike,* which has a very narrow pick-up pattern, only to the front, and must be aimed like a gun to get just the right spot for the source of the sound you are after. Shotgun mikes are used mainly for picking up sound over long distances, because they let so little incidental noise in. Other directional mikes have switchable pick-up patterns that can be varied for different applications.

All microphones have one purpose: to receive sound vibrations and convert these vibrations to electrical impulses. There are five methods which microphones use to do this, and all mikes fall into one of the five categories. The first two are the *crystal* and *ceramic* microphones. These mikes are the cheapest you can buy and quality is also the lowest. Avoid crystal and ceramic mikes if you can. The additional money needed for a higher-quality mike will more than pay back your investment.

The next kind of microphone is known as a *ribbon mike.* Ribbon mikes were most often used in radio, and you can still get hold of them. They are of very high quality and quite expensive. The problem is that they are extremely sensitive to shock and must be treated with great care. They should never be used outside, since wind can damage them. The best situation for the use of a ribbon mike is to have it permanently mounted in one spot for use by a narrator.

The most popular mike in use in recording studios and broadcast radio and television is the *condenser* microphone. Condenser mikes give the most natural sound of any microphone, with a wide frequency response. These superior mikes are quite durable and are becoming more so, if you can believe the manufacturers' claims. From our point of view, the big drawback to condenser mikes is their high price. These are by far the most expensive mikes for many reasons, mainly bcause they must have a pre-amp built right into the body of the mike. If you can afford the best in audio equipment, get a condenser microphone. As an example of their value, *used* Nuemann condenser mikes are selling for around $300.

The last and most popular in our price range is the rugged *dynamic mike*. It receives sound on a pressure-sensitive diaphragm, and as the diaphragm vibrates to the pressure of the sound waves, electrical charges are produced. Dynamic mikes are moderately priced and are good for both studio and outdoor operations. They have good frequency response, which means that dynamic mikes are capable of picking up sounds that have greatly varying frequencies. Also, unlike the ribbon mike, they are relatively unaffected by temperature changes. These are by far the best all-around microphones and are highly recommended.

There are two other classifications of microphones that are important to understand. These classifications deal with the electrical

Dynamic microphone.

40

resistance or *impedance* of a mike, which can be either *high* or *low*. For some reason, many vtr's have *high impedance* mike inputs. The impedance of a microphone has little to do with the kind of mike that it is. The only thing that should concern you about impedance is the length of the mike cable. You should not attempt to use a mike cable any longer than 10 feet with a high impedance mike. When using a cable longer than this, a distinct hum will be detected on the audio track of your recording, which is quite unacceptable.

If you intend to operate a mike farther than 10 feet away from your recorder or mixer, you must use a *low impedance* microphone. Low impedance mikes can be operated hundreds of feet away from the vtr with no problem. You will have to purchase a low to high impedance *transformer,* so that you will be able to feed the mike into the recorder. The transformers are inexpensive and can be used for so many things that they are an excellent investment. Take your low impedance mike as far as you like from the recorder, and run the cable all the way back. Then, just before the vtr itself, feed it into the transformer, and then into the vtr. Low impedance mikes are slightly more expensive than high, but well worth it. You should not have to spend much more than $50 for a mike and transformer of good quality.

In order to have some control over the audio that you feed the vtr, especially ones that come equipped with *automatic gain control* (AGC), you should have an audio mixer. Machines that come with AGC, automatically control the level of the audio signal. This is an invaluable device in a one-person Porta-Pak situation

Audio mixer.

VU meter with audio level set too high.

VU meter with audio level set properly.

where you just do not have the time or the extra hands to check audio levels.

Many times, when there is a silent period during the taping, the AGC circuit will amplify the noise inherent to your system, and you will get a very annoying humming or buzzing. An *audio mixer* lets you set the levels you feel are proper for a particular scene. Simple inexpensive mixers can be had for under $50, but these do not come with VU meters.

A *VU meter* measures volume units in decibels, or *db*. The meter has two zones on its face. One is usually white or light yellow, and it goes into a red zone. The point at which the light-colored bar changes into a red one is the zero db point. This is the optimum audio level. A needle fluctuates back and forth across the face of the meter as the intensity of the audio signal changes. If it remains in the red zone all the time, serious distortion will result, since this signifies that the audio portion is too strong. The best place to try to keep the needle is in the center portion of the meter. Occasional peaks into the red area are acceptable, but not for prolonged periods of time.

Audio mixers control the strength of the signals coming into them by means of *potentiometers,* or *pots.* There are dials on the front of the mixer that control the pots, and you raise or lower the audio signal by looking at the VU meter and adjusting the signal accordingly. Mixers with VU meters and up to five pots can be purchased for under $200. These can be *stacked,* or added on to, to create sophisticated mixers capable of mixing any number of audio sources, such as mikes, turntables, audio tape recorders, and other vtr's. If you plan on using and mixing sounds from other sources, a mixer is essential.

Very few vtr's will allow you to mix audio signals right at the vtr. The only ones that do permit this, have two audio channels, which means that they will allow you to record two separate audio signals. This does not afford you a great deal of flexibility, however, and it does limit you to only two sources. Many recorders have a *high-level* audio input. This is not to be confused with the high impedance mike input. High-level audio signals are those that generally come from mixers, and it is this input you should use to feed in the signal from your mixer, as well as from other vtr's, turnables, and audio tape recorders. Read the instruction manual carefully before attempting to hook anything up to your vtr, particularly audio gear.

Do not attempt to record high-quality musical selections with the mike supplied with a Porta-Pak. It has poor frequency response and the resulting sound will be very inadequate. A much better idea is to record the selection on a good audio tape recorder and carefully dub in the sound after you bring the tape back to your base of operations. Even the Porta-Pak has a audio dubbing facility, and you should make use of it for situations like this. There is no need for the dubbing procedure if you are using good-quality mikes and a

Audio dub function.

mixer. But in any music situation, from taping a friend playing an acoustical guitar to a large band or orchestra, don't ruin your tape by getting bad audio results. Take the extra time involved to set up a good audio tape recorder and do it right. There is no sense in knocking yourself out to get a beautifully constructed video portion, only to have a wavy and unnatural sound track.

When making a dramatic type of tape, you should understand something about the perspective of the sound that you record. *Sound perspective* means that the quality and intensity of the sound must relate to the picture on the screen. In a close-up of a man talking, we would expect to hear his voice clearly, and close up. In other words, the *presence* of the sound must relate to the picture. Cutting to a long shot of a woman in the distance, the audience would be very upset if the presence of the sound of her voice was the same as the nearby man. If both their voices sounded the same, the audio in that scene would not be satisfactory. The woman must sound as far away as she looks, even if the microphone is right next to her. The *gain*, or volume, must be dropped on her mike until it is just faint enough to approximate her distance. The closer the shot of someone, the closer he must sound; the farther away he appears, the more remote he should sound.

44

Male Cannon plug.

Female Cannon plug.

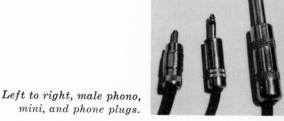

Left to right, male phono, mini, and phone plugs.

Proper perspective, or presence, is essential to good audio. It will take some experimenting with your mixer, but you will appreciate the results. In this case, automatic gain control would be a distinct handicap. The machine would attempt to equalize both speakers, with the result that the presence of neither would sound correct. If your machine gives you the option of overriding the AGC circuit, as many do, now is the time to exercise your option.

When dealing with audio, you will spend a lot of time with the various methods of hooking one piece of equipment up to another. This is accomplished by means of *audio connectors*. There are four basic kinds of connectors, and you will get to know each of them very well. All connections on the machine are called *jacks,* and are also referred to as "female," for obviously chauvinistic reasons. Connectors on cables are called *plugs* and are the "male" connectors. *Cannon* connectors are almost always used for low impedance sources. *Phone* and *RCA* (sometimes known as "phono" to add to the confusion) connectors are mostly for high-level and high impedance connections. The *mini* connector is used for everything, high and low. Remember, you can't tell the impedance of a source by its connector! This is one area where some standardization is really needed and let's hope it is forthcoming.

With this wide variety of connectors in use you will find that you will need an almost unlimited supply of adaptors to go from one type to another. Try as you may, it will be virtually impossible for you to standardize your operation on one kind of connector. Make up as many combinations of connectors as you can think of, be creative. Male to female Cannons, male to male phones, male minis to female RCA's are all handy combinations. When the time comes (and it will always be an emergency), chances are that you will not have the adaptor that you need for that situation. Keep a large supply of assorted connectors and audio cable on hand. A section on how to make up adaptors, or *patch cords*, is included in Appendix B. Please refer to it, since knowing how to solder is an absolute must when quick solutions are required.

CHAPTER 6

THE PORTA-PAK

Porta-Paks are the synthesis of all the information contained in the previous chapters. They are also the *raison d'être* for this book, since the Media Revolution will be abetted by the widespread use of Porta-Paks. Porta-Paks make it impossible for any one group to control the flow of televised information. "The bias of record, storage, and instant playback, punctures the estranging mythology of technology as something to be operated and therefore controlled by an elite" (Shamberg, p. 21). In other words, anyone can operate a Porta-Pak and produce programming that is pleasing to watch, and which is equally informative. This programming has no need to be careful of vested interests, and can present information to the public that is taboo for broadcast television. The Media Revolution is also the Information Access Revolution.

Porta-Pak is a generic term that refers to the equipment produced that provides as a self-contained system: a small portable camera, a video tape recorder, a microphone, and sometimes, playback capability. The Sony Rover Porta-Pak is by far the most popular model. More people own this model than any other. For this reason, most of the information in this chapter will be related to the Sony Rover. All information, however, applies to all Porta-Paks in general.

Porta-Paks are battery operated, but they can also use AC 110 volt house current. They can be used anywhere where there is sufficient light, and anywhere that you can carry them.

47

Sony Rover II. Courtesy Sony Corp.

The batteries supplied with Porta-Paks last about forty-five minutes, and take up to eight hours to recharge fully. Longer-lasting batteries are available from Sony that will last for three hours, but they are heavy and do not fit into the machine itself. People have used motorcycle batteries and movie camera battery belts that give four hours of record and playback time, and this seems to be the best solution. The belts are not too cumbersome, and not terribly expensive.

The vtr battery pack is quite cumbersome in its original design. The manufacturers set it up for you to carry over your shoulder, but unfortunately, the human shoulder was not designed to carry much weight for long periods of time. After about ten minutes or so, you tend to get a little shaky. With conditioning and much practice, you will be able to prolong your endurance to pain for a half hour, but there is no need for this. You can buy an inexpensive back pack frame from any camping supply dealer and easily modify it to accept the vtr package. If you mount it sideways on the frame, you will be able to control the vtr functions by reaching around with your free hand. The problem is that you have no way to see how much time you have left, or to see if the tape is running through the machine

48

properly. It is highly recommended that shooting with Porta-Paks be a two-man operation: one to hold the camera, and the other to carry the vtr and also to serve as audio man when using an external mike. If you build a packframe for your machine, you can mount a motor-cycle battery on the frame, as well, and save the expense of either the long-life Sony battery—or the movie battery belt.

The cameras supplied with a Porta-Pak are meant to be hand-held, but they can be tripod-mounted. They all have some kind of pistol grip, and for some reason they all look something like Super 8 movie cameras. This is really unfortunate. There is absolutely no reason for the lens, the electronics, and the viewfinder to be all in one package. There have been many times when in order to get just the perfect camera angle, we have had to become contortionists and bend into unnatural angles, just to get a look through the viewfinder.

Since the only optics that are involved are from the lens to the faceplate of the vidicon, why not put just the lens and vidicon and essential electronics into a small package that could be held in the palm of your hand? The rest of the electronics could be contained in the vtr/battery pack, either on a back pack or strapped to the body, like a belt. The viewfinder could go on a head band, and it

Pack frame for Porta-Pak.

Porta-Pak camera with wide-angle lens.   *The ideal Porta-Pak.*

could be flipped down in front of an eye, or up out of the way when not needed.

The vtr/battery pack could be better designed so as to be carried more comfortably on the back or in some other configuration, and the controls could be made much more accessible. With this sort of setup, you would merely point your hand at the object you wish to tape, and you would be in business. This is a dream configuration, but let us hope that the manufacturers use some ingenuity in design as well as function in the next generation of Porta-Paks.

The Porta-Pak camera offers fairly sharp pictures with a resolution higher than the vtr can record. The new cameras come with a 4:1 zoom lens, which is not a bad place to start from. One of your first investments should be the addition of a wide-angle lens. Porta-Paks use *C-mount* lenses, which are readily available in camera stores. The C-mount lens that a vidicon camera uses is the same as for a 16mm movie camera, so you can use any C-mount lens made for movie cameras with no special adaptors. You can even get an adaptor that will enable you to use a 35mm still camera lens on your camera, but this is not recommended for general use since the edges of the pictures will not appear to be as sharp as the center.

The best wide-angle lens to use is either a 10mm or an 8½mm. The 8½mm lens has the added value of also being a very fast lens. That is, it opens up to f 1.5, which will allow you to shoot in relatively low-light situations. There is some distortion with these lenses, but it is not unacceptable.

You can walk around while taping with a wide-angle lens, for

50

a true *cinéma vérité* style. This gives a very life-like look to your tape, and should always be used when that effect is needed. After your initial fun with the zoom lens supplied with the camera, you will find the wide-angle lens to be so valuable that you will be using it almost all the time.

The Porta-Pak vtr pack weighs about 15 pounds and, as has been mentioned, is cumbersome to carry around. One way to avoid this is to get a longer camera cable. (Such cables can be purchased in lengths up to 32 feet.) This will allow you to set the recorder down in one spot, and still have a rather wide area in which to move around.

Zoom lens and 8½ mm wide-angle lens for Porta-Pak.

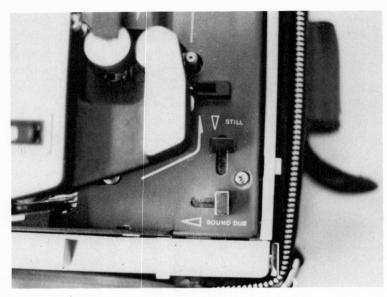

Still frame and audio dub controls.

Also, by leaving it in one spot while you are moving around and taping, you will prevent some of the picture instability that results from bumping the pack around while taping.

All recording functions on the Porta-Pak are AGC. The camera sets itself automatically, as does the recorder for audio and video levels. These functions can be overridden by a technician, but unless you are really technically adept, don't attempt this conversion yourself. If you have manual overriding controls put onto your machine, make sure that these functions can be switched back to AGC. This is mandatory for one-man operation.

The controls that Sony has left for humans are important ones. The Sony Rover allows you to dub in sound over pre-recorded video information, which is something that even some one-inch machines can't do. The vtr has a freeze frame switch, which is very handy for identification purposes and for noting any details in the scene that you may have wanted to check. It can also be used in editing as described in Chapter 16 on special effects. The other control you have is a tracking knob for playback. This is not one of the most effective tracking controls I have ever seen, but let's be thankful that it is there. You rotate the knob until the best picture obtainable

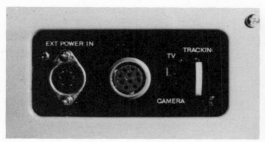

Jack panel of Porta-Pak.   *Sony 10-pin connector.*

is seen on the screen. Tracking on the Rover is strictly a visual function of the operator. On more expensive machines, there is a dial to help set the proper tracking position. There is also a plug on the vtr for an earphone jack. This is not much good during recording, but it does come in handy during playback, since there is no audio amplifier. You can also use this plug as an audio-out point, and feed the audio into a sound system.

The plugs on the Sony Rover vtr are hard to work with. They are Sony connector plugs, and you need special Sony jacks to go in and out with video. Other systems use standard coaxial cable connectors, which makes things much simpler.

You can get around the Sony system by using the earphone plug for audio-out, and the external mike plug for audio-in. To get video-out into a monitor, for example, without the use of an RF adaptor, you will need a piece of coaxial cable that is stripped down to the copper on one end. Give yourself about half an inch of bare copper at this end, and put a standard coax jack on the other end of the cable, for plugging into the monitor. If you look closely at the Sony con-

RF out jack.   *Earphone and external microphone jack.*

Stripped coaxial cable in #3 hole of Porta-Pak, for video out to a monitor.

nector, you will see that the pins and holes (jacks and plugs) are numbered. Insert the bare end of the cable into the #3 hole of the Sony plug in the vtr, and attach the other end to the monitor. There you have it! An easy way to defeat the Sony ten-pin connector riddle.

All Porta-Paks have built-in mikes and/or plugs for an external microphone. The built-in mikes are either in or on the camera, which means they are always pointed at the subject of the video, which is not always the sound source. Since the mikes are omnidirectional, this is not much of a drawback when shooting indoors. If you can keep within 15 feet of your subject, the audio won't be too bad. Unless you are much closer outside, the mikes will not be very good.

Also, because the mike is mounted in the camera, it will pick up the sound of the zoom lens reaching a stop. The most annoying sound it picks up, however, is the click made when starting and stopping the camera. This click comes from the trigger on the pistol grip. Some people have gone so far as to install micro-switches on their cameras to eliminate this noise. The use of an external mike shuts the camera's mike off, so when using another microphone, you lose those sounds as well as the knocking of the lens cap on tripod legs (a common one, if you attach the lens cap the way Sony would like you to) and the sounds the cameraman makes, such as breathing and making comments he might regret later. When the Porta-Pak is being operated in a one-man situation, the built-in mike is

54

Built-in microphone (omnidirectional).

essential. When you can use more than one person, however, it is always best to use an external mike.

There are two problems that we encounter all the time, and you should be aware of them, since they are chronic to all Sony Porta-Paks. The first is that the tape has a nasty habit of winding itself around the capstan roller. When you are taping, there is no way to know that this is happening. Once you've discovered that yards and yards of tape are wound up in a tight little circle around the capstan, it is a painstakingly slow process to unwind it. No matter

Handle and trigger for Porta-Pak camera.

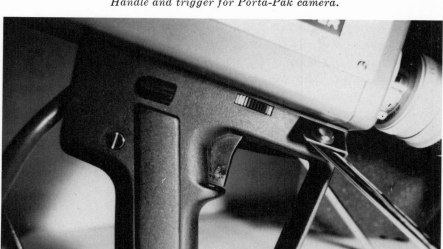

Tape wound up on capstan roller.

how carefully you unwind the tape, there will be some that got too cinched and wrinkled and must be discarded. Invariably, this will be an important piece of tape, so you should take steps to try to avoid this situation.

As far as we have been able to determine, this problem has two causes. The first is that the capstan rollers are dirty, and the tape will not pass smoothly by. Always keep all parts of your machine as clean as possible, especially all the rollers. Alcohol or Freon is best for this purpose.

The other cause of this problem is that sometimes the top of the case in which the vtr is housed does not fit properly. When you close it, the top rubs against either the supply or take-up reel, and this causes uneven tension, which results in poor picture quality and/or the tape getting caught around the capstan. Always check to make sure that your case was not banged or dented in such a way that it will interfere with the tape path.

The other problem we have experienced with Sony Porta-Paks is improper threading of the tape. The vtr's have clearly labeled threading paths, but for some reason, no matter how many times you have threaded a machine, mistakes will happen every once in a while. The critical point is again at the capstan roller. Very often people put the tape on the outside of the pressure roller, where it

56

Tape threaded on wrong side of capstan roller.

Tape threaded correctly.

looks as if it should go. Unfortunately, as is so often the case, looks are deceiving. The tape *must* go between the capstan roller and the tape guide. If it doesn't, there will appear to be severe tracking problems on playback and much breakup on the screen. If you should experience this, don't call a technician until you check to see how the machine was threaded.

Porta-Paks are the newest in a series of exciting technological advancements that caught most of us off guard. They will prove to be, I feel, one of the most important breakthroughs ever, in the fields of art, science, and education. With cable television becoming more and more widespread, vast new areas of information distribution are upon us. With these areas, information needs will arise, and these needs will best be filled by the Porta-Pak. It is one of the greatest methods of information-gathering yet devised, since it allows anyone the opportunity to document his own personal feelings and observations in a way that can be seen by millions of people. The Porta-Pak is one of the main causes of, and reasons for, the Media Revolution.

CHAPTER 7

LIGHTING

An electrographer working with portable video gear has so few problems with lighting that his brother craftsmen in film become quite jealous when this subject comes up. Cinematographers are likely to change the subject and discuss the psychological differences between video and film rather than admit to the ease with which the electographer can walk into practically any situation and begin recording without first "lighting the set."

A filmmaker almost always must amend natural conditions before he can begin exposing film. It is often necessary to go to extreme lengths to hide lighting equipment. Sometimes objects must be added to a scene for the sole purpose of hiding a lighting instrument.

One of the most important features of portable video is that it records precisely what is taking place. Additional, subjective elements are not introduced into a situation; persons and events being recorded need not be manipulated or made uncomfortable by glaring lights. Our medium, above all others, is reality-oriented. Even large-scale, network-type television drama has a different impact than film. We work with a communications medium that is dramatic, not a dramatic one that communicates.

Portable video is designed to operate in "normal" lighting conditions: in classrooms with fluorescent lights, in living rooms with incandescent lighting, and of course, in outdoor daylight. Good-quality

58

pictures can be recorded in almost any situation without additional lighting or modification of existing lighting. However, there are ways of taking advantage of available light that can enhance the recorded image.

There are three basic types of lighting: *front light* (or *key* light), *side light* (or *fill* light), and *back light* (or *rim* light).

Outdoors, the main lighting instrument we use is the sun. By positioning yourself at varying angles around the subject, the sun can become any of the above types of lighting.

There is one shot you must never, ever, use, and that is a shot of the sun. The absolute rule of video is to *NEVER* point the camera into the sun or *any* bright light! If you do, the image will be *burned in* on the plate of the camera pickup tube. A burn-in occurs when an overpowering light force is focused onto the pickup tube. The electrons that become "excited" in order to change the optical image to an electronic one, "remember" this image. The tube then transmits a grey negative of that image over the subsequent shots taken. Television cameras are very sensitive to burn-in, and extreme care must be taken to avoid this condition.

Another image that can cause a burn is white lettering on a black background that is brightly lit, or anything that has strong

Removing burn by panning over grey surface.

Removing burn by aiming camera at white surface reflecting bright light.

black-and-white contrast. The white letters will appear in negative long after you have taken the shot.

If a burn-in has occurred, you must remove it as soon as possible. There are three ways I would recommend to eliminate the burn. First, for a rather insevere burn, pan the camera back and forth over a neutral surface, such as a floor. For more severe burns, defocus the camera totally and aim it into a diffused light source. This can be harmful and care should be taken. This can be accomplished by putting some cheesecloth or a T-shirt, over a scoop, and pointing the camera at the cheesecloth. You can also aim a very bright light, such as a quartz light, onto a white piece of paper and aim the camera at that. If it is a sunny day, you can take the camera and the white paper outside and use the sun to illuminate the paper. I must emphasize again that these last methods are only for severe burns and extreme care must be taken in using them.

Needless to say, when using the sun as a back light, you must be very careful.

There are instances in electrography when one must control the light, for example, at night, and in drama or staged instances. For that reason, I feel that a basic knowledge of lighting techniques and instruments is essential.

60

Removing burn by aiming camera at white surface reflecting sunlight.

The type of lighting instrument most beneficial to our needs is the *quartz lamp.* Recent innovations in lighting technology have given us this product, which is smaller, brighter, lighter, and uses less electricity than incandescent lamps.

These lamps are usually quartz iodine or tungsten halogen. They burn at extremely high temperatures and an ordinary glass bulb would quickly explode at these temperatures, so "quartz," or a specially designed glass, is used instead.

Certain precautions are necessary when using quartz lighting.

Quartz lamp in paper covering.

61

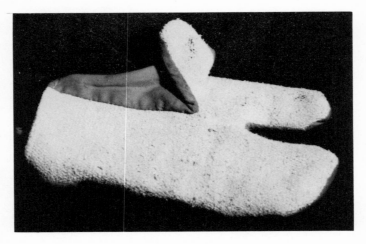

Quartz mitt.

Never touch the surface of the lamp itself. Handle it only by the ceramic edges or with the paper in which the bulb is wrapped. The chemical composition of the quartz glass is such that the oil from your fingers will cause the glass to deteriorate, and this can cause an explosion that can splatter hot molten quartz glass in all directions. This should be an inducement not to handle the bulb excessively.

Also, always wear asbestos gloves while handling a quartz-lit lighting instrument. As I have said, the lamp burns at a very high temperature, and consequently the instrument becomes very hot.

100 watt incandescent light bulb and 650 watt quartz lamp.

Fresnel spot light with barn doors.

Asbestos gloves, or "quartz mitts" as they are called, are cheap, about $5 a pair, and well worth the protection they give your hands.

These safety tips are not meant to frighten you about quartz lighting. Properly handled, quartz is the best lighting that exists. After all, quartz was to the lighting industry what portable video was to the television industry.

There are numerous types of instruments in a fully equipped television studio, certainly more than we would ever need. The ones that most concern us are *fresnels* (pronounced frā·nel′), *scoops,* and *broads.*

The *fresnel* spotlight is so called because of its fresnel lens. This is the most widely used light of all. It is flexible, and throws a great deal of light. Its main feature is that you can adjust the fresnel to

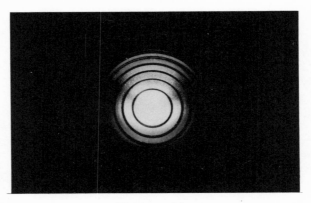

The fresnel lens.

throw a wide flooded beam of light, or a "spotted down" circle of light, or anything in between. The fresnel is used for key and back lighting.

The *scoop*, so called because of its shape, is a floodlight. It has no lens, and is used for fill lighting. A good example of the efficiency of quartz lamps is that a 500w quartz scoop will throw about as much light as a 1500w incandescent scoop.

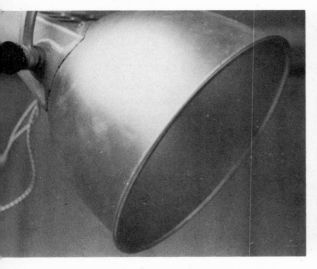

Side view of 1,000 watt quartz scoop.

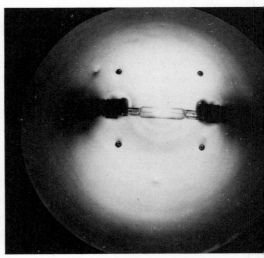

Front view of 1,000 watt quartz scoop.

Quartz broad.

A *broad* is also mainly a floodlight, but since it will accept barn-doors, it is used somewhat differently.

Barndoors fit over the front of fresnels and broads, and they enable you to cut off light from areas you don't want lit.

Before you begin modeling the lighting of a scene, there must be a sufficient amount of base light. A studio vidicon camera needs about 150–200 foot candles, Plumbicon only around 75–100 foot candles. Portable video operates on considerably less. Low-light level cameras are available that need practically no light; however, they

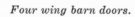

Four wing barn doors.

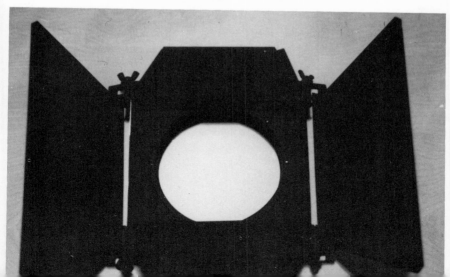

are expensive, and generally used for surveillance. At any rate, when a camera receives less than its base level of light, the signal-to-noise ratio comes into effect. Every picture has a certain amount of "noise." Noise looks like a "grainy" photograph. It is caused by the natural movement of electrons on the pickup tube and screen or raster. When not enough light is on the subject, the noise will be stronger than the signal. Brightly lit subjects produce a strong signal, and the inherent noise is no longer noticeable.

Basic lighting consists of placing lighting instruments in such a way that they fulfill the functions of the *key light*, the *back light*, and the *fill light*.

The *key light*, usually a fresnel, but sometimes a broad, is placed in front of and slightly at an angle to the subject. The *back light* is hung on a stand or a wall, directly behind and above the subject. This provides a rim of light that brightens the top of the subject, as well as separating it from the background. It gives much more of a three-dimensional effect to a two-dimensional picture. Fresnels and broads are used as back lights.

At this point, you will notice some sharp shadows have been created on the subject. The harshness of the shadows is eliminated by placing a *fill light*, the scoop, at the same angle as the fresnel, except off to the other side. This will soften the dark spots, and make a more pleasing picture.

Lighting instruments are usually placed well above the subject. However, this is not an inflexible rule. If the key light is placed on a level below that of the subject, an entirely different mood is created.

Basic television lighting works on a brightness ratio between the back light and the key light. If the back light is not bright enough, it will be washed out by the key, and thereby be totally ineffectual. Conversely, if it is too intense, a halo effect will be visible on the screen, eliminating any thought of reality. A general rule to follow is that if the back light is approximately 1½ times as bright as the key, it will give a nice balance to the picture.

An indispensable lighting tool can be made for about 50¢. This is a reflector to be used when shooting outdoors on a sunny day. On very bright days, there may be entirely too much contrast between well-lit areas and shadows. Instead of worrying about portable lighting, you can place your reflector in such a way that it will heighten or soften contrast, depending on where you place it. Take a

66

Front (key) light.

Side (fill) light.

Back (rim) light.

Proper balance of key, fill, and rim light.

piece of 3′ x 3′ sturdy cardboard and cover it with aluminum foil. Always use the dull side, and if you crinkle it up before gluing it to the board, it will really diffuse the light.

A tip on F-stops: If the sun or light source is behind your subject, the subject's face will probably show up too dark. You should open up the lens to a wider setting to bring out details such as these. (See Chapter 10 on the zoom lens.)

CHAPTER 8

MAKING ACTION MOVE

The title of this chapter may be a bit misleading at first; however, give some thought to the limitations of the television screen. Whether a small 6″ screen, or a 25″ color set, the action being viewed is only what was taped originally by you. The viewer has no peripheral vision. This is one of the reasons McLuhan calls television the "cool medium." The size of the screen tends to cool things down. For example, film is a hot medium since it is viewed on a screen many times larger than life. The film *2001: A Space Odyssey,* was a powerful cinematic experience. It is conceivable that at some point one of the networks will purchase broadcast rights to the film. Imagine the experience of watching *2001* on an 11″ black-and-white receiver! It certainly would not have the same force that it did in a theater with a wide screen and 16 track sound.

During the Democratic Convention in Chicago in 1968, the FCC called CBS to task for its overplaying of the violence in the streets. CBS showed its tapes to the commissioner and proved that out of approximately 50 hours of convention coverage only fewer than 30 minutes actually showed the violence. The reason why all the violent activities tended to stand out in people's memories was that the violence, whether small groups or large, was contained within an average 18″ receiver. This did not make television any "hotter"; all it did was to dramatically show up the contrasts between the

68

politics in the streets, and the yawning, bored, and boring politicians inside the convention center. Had the same scenes been shown in a movie theater (as they graphically were in Haskell Wexler's *Medium Cool*), or broadcast live over radio, an intensely "hot" medium, the reaction worldwide would have been significantly stronger.

Radio is a hot medium, because so much of the action is left entirely up to the listeners' imagination. One has not only peripheral vision, but total vision. There are no limitations, or worries over making action move. Anything can be convincingly put over on radio. (Remember *War of the Worlds*?) Video, however, offers many more fascinating challenges to the artist, as well as to society.

There are some basic rules and guidelines to follow when dealing with the containment of action within the screen. One of the most important of these is the placement of the camera in relation to the direction of the movement. When taping a chase scene, for example, we see the "bad guy" running down the street, followed closely by the "good guy." They move across the screen right to left. If, as the chase continues, the cameraman were to cross the street and tape the runners, it would appear that the roles had been reversed, since the chase would now be moving across the scene from left to right.

If the action is fast-paced and changing direction constantly, switching the sides you shoot from may be acceptable. However, it does tend to be confusing, and if this isn't your intent, always shoot the movement of action from the same side of that action.

One aspect of the medium with which electrographers must be aware, is the possibility of magnification. Educators often attach a camera to a microscope so that an entire class can see the movements of an amoeba, for example. You should take advantage of this effect.

An amoeba may move only an inch or two in its lifetime. However, one could create an amoeba ballet by just filling the screen with a few of the beasties and dubbing an appropriate musical score onto the audio track. Playing this tape through a colorizer (see Chapter 16) will produce a sensuous and vivid program, with considerable action (action that was virtually nonexistent until you made it move).

Once, while taping a group of African drummers, I was forced to "make the action move." They had worked up a frenzied, driving beat, yet they themselves were hardly moving. I moved in for close-ups of the concentration on their faces, but it didn't match the audio.

Making the Media Revolution

When I began to cut back and forth between their hands streaking across the heads of the drums, and the slow rhythmic beat of their feet, the effect of the tape soared.

Generally, when there is little or no apparent action, shoot tight close-ups of whatever movement there may be. The magnifying aspects of television will increase the movement. Also, contrasting different types of action, within the same scene, will produce interesting effects. In fencing, for example, there are extremes of action that can be capitalized upon. A lingering long shot of both contestants to set the scene and point-out to the viewer the differences between the two makes a good opening shot. This might be followed by a slow zoom-in to one and then the other of the fencers as the action builds in intensity. Continue the zoom-in to the sparkling, quivering, slashing tips of the swords themselves. (The scenes must be brightly lit and shot against a dark background.) We have now manipulated the scene to provide a good deal of action and nice movement as the athletes flow from one side of the screen to the other. The action builds in speed as we increase the amount of movement actually happening, by filling the screen with smaller bits of the action (by using close-ups). We reach the maximum possible action as the swords' tips fill the screen. To contrast this, a quick cut to a close-up of the outstretched rear hand of each fencer. Cutting, dissolving, or panning between the slow deliberate movements of the rear hands and the quick bites of the sword tips makes for an interesting method of making action move, the way you manipulated it.

One of the nicest things about video, is that the mass audience already understands it as a perfect method of viewing action. One can go out to a mammoth stadium on a freezing day, and watch a professional football game. There is another option, and that is to watch the game on television. Here, you always seem to be about 10 feet above and slightly off to the side of the players. In the stadium, you might be hundreds of feet from the action. The cameras are probably farther away than that. However, with long lenses, good cameramen, and a working knowledge of the game, a good director can always pinpoint action on the field, and even show it again on instant replay. People have become accustomed to television's unique ability to be at the spot where the action takes place. However, that is broadcast, network-type television. People don't expect too much from portable video, for the simple reason that they are unaware of its existence.

70

We can take advantage of viewer habits. When the viewers at home sat down and watched the Washington peace moratoriums, what they saw was the mass of people from what seemed like about 10 feet above the crowd, and slightly off to the side. Only the home viewers actually saw the speakers. However, there were a number of people in Washington with Rovers. Where the people at home saw newsmen discussing their opinions of the action, anyone who has seen the tapes made by the portable video people, saw the demonstration. No one's expert opinion was needed. With a Rover, the video people were part of the experience, not merely a recorder of it.

When recording something like a large demonstration, it is advisable to watch the flow patterns of the demonstrators. Get a feel for the types of action as well as the direction. Some nice tapes can be made of orderly lines of marchers, as well as of the police, for example. Feet, arms, toes, hands, heads, flags, and any other small moving parts of other things should be recorded in motion. Also, take long shots of groups in motion, for example, people dancing and

Chase from right to left on one side of street
and from left to right on other side.

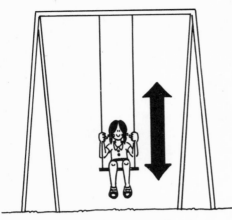

*Child on swing from front,
showing up and down motion.*

*Child on swing from side,
showing horizontal arc movement.*

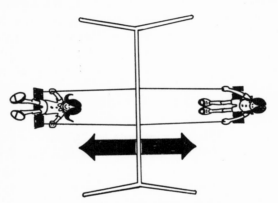

*Child on swing from top,
showing back and forth movement.*

swaying, and small groups of people moving about. All of the above actions, and more, can then either be edited together, juxtaposing mass action with individual motion, or you can play a number of tapes back on multiple monitors to really give a feeling of what it was like to be involved, to be in the midst of a vast amount of action.

You can make the same action move in a number of different ways. One of the most important aspects of recording motion, is knowing how to look at its direction. You must look at action, or motion, in respect to its direction on the screen.

The classic example is a child on a swing. Recording the swing in motion from directly in front, will give the impression of a back-and-forth motion, but it will also be predominantly an up-and-down motion. On playback, the swing will appear to move mostly in an up-and-down direction. If you move the camera to a point off to one side, it will also show an up-and-down motion, but this time, predominantly in an horizontal direction, or basically an arc. If you were to look from directly above at the same child swinging, the direction of the action would be from side to side. If you remain in the same spot and change the camera angle, you can have the swing move in any direction you please. By proper camera placement, in regard to the direction of the action, the motion of that action on the screen is entirely up to the cameraman, and is under his control.

This is an important technique when you are creating continuity. The action must flow steadily from scene to scene. If you were cutting from the fencers, for example, to the girl on the swing, it would be vital to match the directions of the action. A pleasing series of shots might be cutting from the marchers swaying back and forth, to the child swinging, shot from the side, to a fencer lunging. All this action is moving horizontally, and when seen in a series of shots edited together, the flow and direction of the action are smooth.

An important thing to keep in mind is the nature of this medium. Portable video, at present, is not an easily editable medium. There are editing facilities available (see Chapter 15), but they are not perfect. The less you have to depend on them, the better off your tape will be. Because of this, you must always be thinking ahead to your next shots. You must use your creative abilities to make the most out of whatever action you are recording. You can make action move the way you want it to, and you can determine its direction and relative importance (depending upon how much of it fills the screen) to the shot. You are the manipulator of the movement to be seen on the screen. Don't allow the action to manipulate you, unless that is your intent.

One of the best ways to get action to move the way you want it to, is to move around it yourself. This will be discussed in the next chapter. Since you are portable, get yourself involved with the flows of the action you are recording. Become a part of it, flow with it, and move around and through it. Once you are a part of the action, and flowing together with it, you are not only making the action move, but helping it to do so.

CHAPTER 9

MAKING THE CAMERA MOVE

All movement that has been discussed up to this point has concerned itself with the action of the subject. However, in producing a video tape, the camera does not often remain stationary while recording an event.

Moving the camera horizontally is called *panning* left or right. Moving the camera vertically is called *tilting* up or down. When you move the camera physically from one spot to another, sideways, the movement is called *trucking*. When you move the camera toward the subject, you *dolly-in;* away from the subject is *dollying-out*.

A basic accessory for portable video is an inexpensive tripod. All cameras have a threaded space for tripod mounting, and it is certainly worthwhile to invest in a sturdy, portable tripod. There are generally two categories of tripods: still photography and motion picture. There is a third—studio television—but this is anything but inexpensive and portable. A good still photography tripod will hold the camera quite steady for telephoto shots, but will not pan smoothly. An inexpensive movie camera tripod is your best bet. The kind you should pick up is one that has a *friction pan head*. The tripod is made with sliding surfaces that are greased. The amount of pressure needed to pan or tilt is controlled by large knobs. By applying the proper amount of pressure, a very smooth pan can be accomplished. We have had very fine results with the tripods that were made for

Panning.

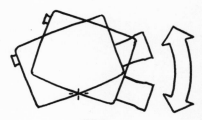

Tilting.

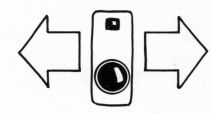

Trucking.

Dollying.

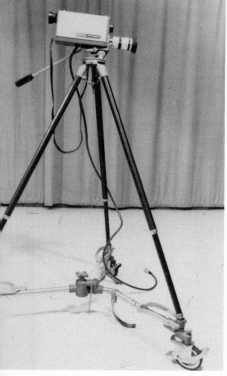

Porta-Pak camera mounted on Cine-Special tripod.

Friction pan head.

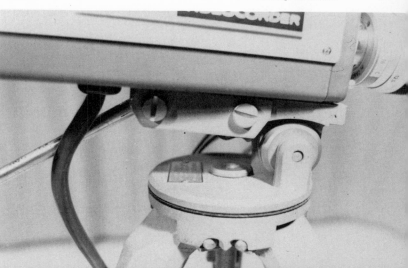

Using the body as a tripod.

the Kodak Cine-Special 16mm camera. There are loads of these around, and can be bought in many camera stores for as little as $15.

For all their value and usefulness, there are times when a tripod is too bulky to bring along, or when the smoothness of a shot is not essential. On these occasions you use a tripod that is always available—your body.

With practice, you can use your body to brace the camera steadily, pan, tilt, and truck just about as smoothly as on a tripod.

Since most portable television cameras are designed to be hand-

76

held, they already have some sort of grip, with a trigger mechanism included to start the tape recording. Hold this unit in one hand. Use the other hand for zooming and focusing when needed. At all other times, the other hand should be bracing the camera. The arm that is supporting the weight of the camera, that of the trigger hand, should be tucked tightly against the body, with the elbow acting as a brace against your stomach. When panning, swivel your entire body from the waist up; this will give a very smooth movement.

When walking with the camera while it is recording, take long sliding steps. This takes a little practice, as do all the body maneuvers mentioned, but will pay off in the smoothness of the finished tape.

The most elementary and common reason for panning, tilting, and trucking the camera is to keep the subject properly framed. If the camera is stationary and is recording a moving subject, the subject appears to move against a stationary background. If you pan along with the subject, keeping it always framed the same way, the subject will appear motionless against a background that is moving in an opposite direction. If you are taping a motorcyclist who is driving left to right across a meadow, you can create two different moods depending upon what you do with the camera. If you want to show how smoothly he rides over the hills and between the wild flowers of the meadow, a steady camera with a wide-angle lens will show him moving about the field. If, on the other hand, you want to show how great it feels to be controlling a powerful machine, whipping along effortlessly across a beautiful field, then a telephoto shot showing just the machine and the rider is what you want. If you follow the action by panning along with him, the scenery will race by in the opposite direction, while the viewer is one with the driver in terms of movement.

Trucking the camera can also create different moods. If you are taping a guitarist sitting on a stool, playing and singing, you can record the event simply by mounting the camera on a tripod and zooming in, at the appropriate times, on his fingers and his face. If you want the tape to be more than just a recording of the event, but to be part of it, then you must move the camera around the stationary subject. Gliding around him, slowly and smoothly, in time to the beat, and in mood with the piece, you can create a tape that is more than a mere recording. Smoothness is the essence that you are after. It takes practice to be able to truck the camera by taking those long

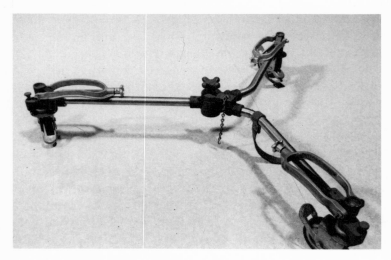

Collapsible dolly attaches to legs of tripod.

sliding, gliding steps. You may want to use some sort of a dolly.

A *camera dolly* is a device that fits wheels under the legs of a tripod. It works fine and will roll a tripod-mounted camera smoothly over any hard, smooth surface.

However, you don't always tape on a hard, smooth surface, and in most cases improvisation is needed. Wheelchairs are universally used as camera dollies for a number of reasons. They are highly maneuverable, they are lightweight, many are collapsible, and they are meant to be pushed. They also have very large rear wheels that roll over cracks, dips, and small bumps. There is no need to mount the camera to the wheelchair frame, since the cameraman's body acts as a shock absorber. The very low dolly that auto mechanics use to roll under cars is also very useful. You can either mount a tripod on it, or have the cameraman lie face up and get low-angle shots, or face forward and get a child's or animal's view of the floor. Just about anything that rolls, including baby carriages, shopping carts, and bicycles, can be used to move the camera. Just remember when using these devices, you must hand-hold the camera to insure smoothness.

If you use bicycles, motorcycles, cars, or anything that vibrates excessively, an additional step should be taken, assuming the subject is nearby. Use a wide-angle lens, or zoom your camera's lens out all the way and hold the camera away from you at arm's length, pointing

78

it at the subject, which at short range and with a wide-angle lens, should be just fine. The weight of the camera will hold it steady, while your outstretched arm will act as a pivot in relation to the camera, thereby reducing the transmission of excessive movement to the camera. (Cf. Kirk Smallman's *Creative Film-Making*.)

If you are trying to show the subjective viewpoint of a character in your production, a moving camera is ideal, particularly a moving portable video camera—it can go anywhere. Portraying rush hour on a crowded subway train, the camera can be right in there, pushing and shoving, recording it all live, as it happens. If your character is going to a department store on the day of a big sale, let the camera go right in with the frenzied shoppers, let it become the subject's eyes. If a chase scene is taped and part of it goes through a field of high grass, run along, with the camera, at arm's length, and let the viewer experience the grass flash by. The camera can take the subject's place, becoming his eyes for the viewer. And, because it *can* go anywhere, take it, and use its portability to create these experiences for the viewer. Use of a wide-angle lens is highly recommended.

Another important form of camera movement, is that which can impart movement to static objects. The best example of this is to make an entire tape out of a series of still pictures. To make this

Using a car as a dolly—note that cameraman holds camera at arm's length for smoothness.

type of production work you need many, large, clear flat pictures, the larger the better. Powerful, moving, and beautiful tapes have been produced very inexpensively using this technique. You will need a tripod and a diffused light source for this setup. Two cameras are most effective, since you can dissolve between them when changing from one picture to the next. Set the cameras up side by side and place half the pictures in front of each camera. Determine the order you wish to shoot them and number them on the back. Place all the odd numbers, first, third, fifth, etc., in front of one camera, and the even ones, the second, fourth, sixth, etc., in front of the other. A music stand makes an ideal, inexpensive, and portable visual holder for all kinds of television graphics. Now look at each picture closely and determine how you want to present it. You can show the entire picture, then slowly zoom in to one part of it, and then pan evenly around the picture showing other details, thoroughly examining and exploring it. You may never want to show the entire picture at once; different bits of a single picture can be shown in different parts of the production. If you have a picture of an airplane facing camera-right, you can pan left across the picture and create an illusion of the plane moving.

A carefully selected musical background is very important. The music should complement the pictures, and more importantly, the camera movement should keep time with the music.

One of my students made an exciting tape called "Woodstock" which made use of this technique. Pictures were taken out of magazines that described the event. They were mounted on stiff board (cardboard or oaktag is perfect; you can mount them with rubber cement, or with a photographic dry mounting press), and put in order. Music was taken from the album "Woodstock," and a very inexpensive program was made very effectively about the concert, by someone who was not even there.

Constant movement is not necessary, and the movement across the face of any picture should be determined by what you want to show in the picture, the mood you are trying to create, and the tempo of your musical background. If there is just a narrator's voice, then movement is, of course, determined by the dialogue.

This type of production can be accomplished even if you don't have two cameras or a switcher fader. If you don't have two cameras, you can shoot the odd-numbered pictures on one tape, and the evens

Black card and picture on flip stand.

on another, and then edit them together. This will involve a good deal of time and effort, and is not recommended. A much simpler method would be to mount a black card or piece of cloth next to the pictures, and when finished with one picture, pan over to the black card, slide the next picture in, and pan the camera back over to that picture.

Camera movement is essential to good electrography. Making the camera move in, around, and across the subject is an important way to set and capture moods. Deciding to move or not to move the camera is your decision, as is the manner in which you move it. However, since video tape is an erasable medium, I recommend you try out a number of different moves, play around with it a little, experiment, and you may discover an exciting new shot.

In conventional television, the director literally "calls the shots." In our type of electrography, it is most often the cameraman who must make the instant decisions on camera movement. For this reason, I include some information on composition and framing techniques in this chapter on camera techniques.

This book cannot teach you how to artfully compose a picture. This is not necessarily a talent you must be born with. However, if you are not, it takes a considerable amount of practice and experience to be able to set up your shots in a pleasing and satisfying manner.

81

Symmetrical framing, with subject in center. *Nonsymmetrical framing, with subject off center.*

Good composition includes having good black-and-white, as well as color, contrast, and making sure that all dimensions of the shot, the various planes and shapes, are arranged both artistically and with the proper stress given to the correct portions of the frame.

There are three important aspects of good framing in the television format. They are *symmetry, equilibrium,* and *balance* (Zettl, p. 421). When you place an object in the exact center of the screen, the picture is evenly divided, or symmetrical. More often than not, this type of framing is not pleasing to the viewer. A more pleasant shot is to set the object slightly to one side, just above or below the center. If, however, there is no background, and you are only showing one object or person, then you should frame it directly in the middle of the frame, symmetrically.

All pictures have equilibrium. They are either stable, unstable, or neutral (Zettl, p. 422). A shot of a cowboy with his boots planted firmly on the prairie grass is a picture that has a stable equilibrium. A scene of the same cowboy about to fall off a bucking bronco would be an unstable shot. Another kind of unstable shot is to shoot while the camera is tilted. This greatly disturbs the equilibrium of the picture, and can be used for dramatic effect. Neutral equilibrium is observed in a shot of the cowboy lying on his side on the ground, in no trouble of disturbing our sense of security about the picture, but not anchored to the ground or as stable as he was in our first shot. He can be ready to move at any point, and this won't upset the viewer.

82

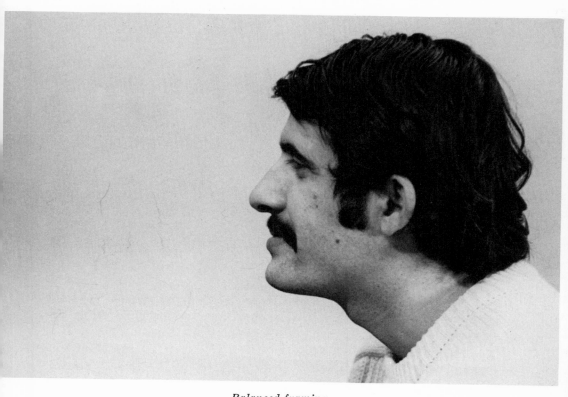

Balanced framing.

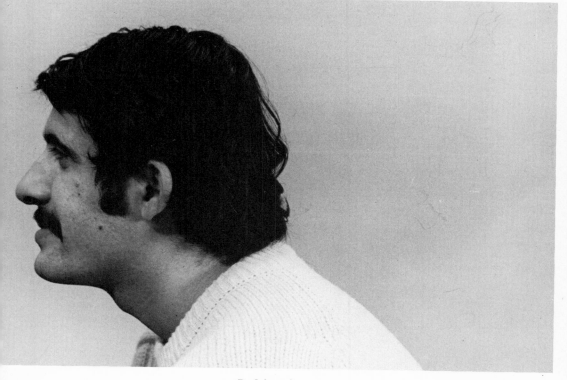

Bad framing.

Keystone effect.

All the objects in a frame must be balanced properly so that one area does not overpower any other area in movement, or in the mass of the objects presented. To properly balance a picture of a close-up of someone talking to a person off screen to the right, for example, always leave more room to the right of the speaker's head. Don't frame him in the center of the screen. This empty space will be filled in by the viewer's imagination with respect to the person to whom the speaker is talking. This space takes the listener's place in the picture. If a person is facing the right side of the screen, always leave room on the right side of the screen, ahead of the person. In other words, frame him on the left half of the screen, and leave the right half, the direction in which he is facing, empty. This creates pleasing balance and equilibrium. A poorly balanced picture will have the person's nose "touching" the edge of the screen. This looks very

Proper setup, with no keystoning.

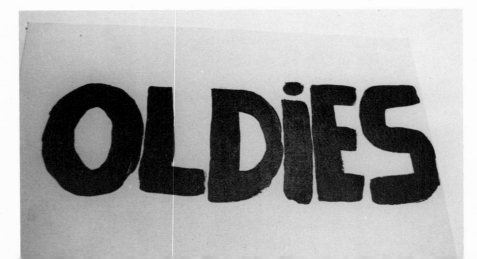

High-angle shot denotes weakness.

bad, and is acceptable only if some event is to take place behind the person on the screen. The best shots to use are those that are on the same level as the object or person being taped. A high- or low-angle shot will make the picture *keystone.* Keystoning is what happens when you are working with two-dimensional media, and the camera is on a different plane, or dimension, than the object. When an object is not precisely head on to the camera, nearly all of the parallel lines that make up that object become no longer parallel. This is particularly evident when lining up title cards in front of a camera. If the card is not head on, the lettering will seem to be "running downhill," that is, the letters will slant either to the left or right, depending on which side of the card is farther away from the camera lens. In order for the lettering to be level, the card must be at the same height as the camera, and exactly parallel to it. The same holds

Low-angle shot denotes strength and power.

true for high- and low-angle shots of people and objects. There will be a certain amount of distortion, depending upon the extremes of the angles from which you are shooting. These shots do have uses, however. A high-angle shot, looking down on a person, tends to make that person appear to be weak and small. A low-angle shot looking up, will make a person seem to be large, strong, and domineering.

CHAPTER 10

HOW TO USE THE ZOOM LENS

Every maker of portable video equipment supplies a zoom lens with his package. Virtually every color camera is made to be used with a zoom lens, and nearly every black-and-white studio camera has a zoom lens. Therefore, let us discuss the special and unique techniques and applications of this type of lens.

Many electrographers have used zoom lenses, but I feel a discussion of the optics is valid. The difference between a "zoomer" and a fixed focal-length lens is inherent in its name. The zoom lens is a sophisticated, complex piece of equipment. The operator can change his field of view by manually changing the focal length of the lens.

Focal length is the distance from the optical center of the lens, to the surface of the camera tube. Focal lengths are measured in millimeters or inches. Long focal-length lenses ("long lens," telephoto lens) have a narrow angle of view. Short focal-length lenses have a wide angle of view.

A verb was created to explain the phenomenon of this appearance of movement. "To zoom" refers not only to the action the cameraman takes in changing the lenses' focal length, but also to the simulated motion.

When one "zooms in," the lens moves to its longest focal length, and the image appears to move toward the camera. When the cameraman "zooms out," or toward the shorter focal length of the optics, the image appears to move away from the camera.

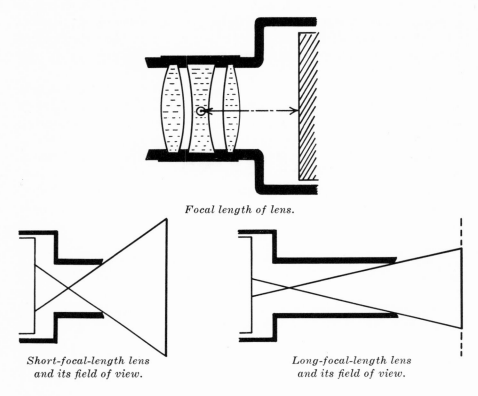

Focal length of lens.

Short-focal-length lens
and its field of view.

Long-focal-length lens
and its field of view.

Zoom lenses vary from about 2:1, to about 20:1. This means that at the widest angle, or fully zoomed out, the field of view is 2, or 20, times the width of the field of view when zoomed in all the way, or to the longest focal length (narrow angle).

Zooming, unfortunately, seems to have replaced "dollying." Dollying is moving the entire camera toward or away from an object, viewed through a fixed focal-length lens. Zooming is much smoother, and requires less expertise. However, a zoom and a dolly both have their individual functions.

When you are dollying in, everything retains its proper perspective. The object itself gets larger as the angle of view of the background get smaller. Zooming, however, creates a different effect (as well as the affect on the viewer). Not only does the object get larger, but the background grows larger, faster than the object itself. This happens because the lens is in its telephoto mode, and is therefore magnifying images more, the farther away they are. An example of this is the centerfield camera in a baseball game, when a long lens is used to show the back of the pitcher as he throws to the batter. Even though the pitcher is about 60 feet closer to the camera than the batter, the batter always appears to be much larger than the pitcher.

Focusing a zoom lens is critical and tricky. I have always taught that the way to focus is to zoom all the way in (even if it's well past the picture you plan to use) and focus with the lens-focusing ring. Then zoom out and adjust the camera focus.

A zoom lens has many internal glass elements, which all move in relation to each other when you zoom or focus. One set of elements slides in and out of the front end of the lens for focusing. The other movable elements determine the focal length. The focus controls come in various configurations, either at the back of the camera or on the lens itself.

Assuming neither the object nor you move very much, you won't have to focus at all during your zoom range. In studio productions it is considered bad technique to focus when your camera is on line or "on the air." However, in the field, with one camera, a few seconds of visible focusing is quite acceptable.

Most studio cameras have two focusing controls: back, or camera, focus, and front, or zoom, focus. The *front focus* is the

Front focusing ring on Porta-Pak camera.

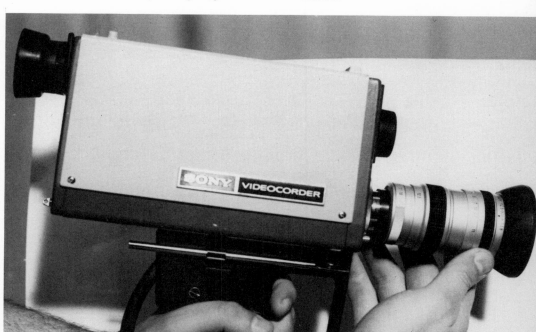

Camera (or back) focus control on studio camera.

control you operate when focusing the lens itself. The *back focus* is a feature found only on studio television cameras. The control moves the entire pickup tube assembly (I-O, Plumbicon, vidicon) nearer or farther from the optical center of the lens, thus changing in effect the focal length.

Once you have "set your focus," that is, zoomed in and focused with the camera focus, you will be in sharp focus throughout the entire zooming range of your camera. That is, however, until either you or your subject move. You must then repeat this procedure as often as the distance between you and the subject changes.

90

How to Use the Zoom Lens

There seems to be some disagreement in the trade as to what order one must follow in order to properly set the focus on a zoom lens. Some say lens focus first, others say camera focus first. However, most portable video gear comes only with the zoom focus. The back focus has already been set in the factory, and this is quite adequate.

This led to some problems with the first group of Sony Rover II's. The lenscap supplied with the package had a ring that was to fit around the lens tube between the lens and the camera. When put together in this manner, the wafer-thin piece of plastic was enough to cause the factory-preset back focus to be set out of adjustment. This caused my engineer friends much consternation. The new lens has been redesigned and this is no longer a problem.

On cameras that do have an adjustable camera focus, one very nice advantage is the minimum focusing distance. On zoom lenses, the closest you can get is usually no less than 3 to 6 feet. This is often not close enough, even when fully zoomed in, to achieve the extreme close-up you desire. With a camera focus control, you can rack the pickup tube assembly back far enough to get a sharp focus on an object normally too close to shoot. However, this throws out any adjustments you may have made, and you cannot zoom without totally losing the picture. Any zooming movement with the camera in this mode will result in an image that is absolutely out of focus. This is a nice effect at times, but usually is more of a nuisance.

It is a principle of optics that a lens with a short focal length (a wide-angle lens) has a great depth of field, while a long lens (telephoto) has a very short depth of field. Since a zoom lens has a variable focal length, you have an infinite number of depths of field with which to work.

Depth of field is an interesting area to work with. Depending on what you wish to emphasize on screen, you should choose your lens, and its focal length accordingly.

Follow focusing is a very beautiful and effective technique. This is accomplished by rotating the lens-focusing ring to maintain focus on a moving subject. You can also change points of interest within the field of view by changing the focus along a line of objects, bringing one after another into and out of focus.

Another very nice effect is to move the camera slowly away from an object, while zooming in at the same rate. This maintains the size of the subject, but totally changes the relative sizes of objects in the foreground as well as the background.

A good guideline to follow about depth of field is, the farther away from the camera an object is, the greater the depth of field. The closer the object, the smaller the depth of field.

The other determinative of depth of field is the size of the lens opening, or *F-stop*. With the lens wide open, a small F-stop, the depth of field is at its most shallow. With the lens stopped down, at the highest F-stop, the depth of field is at its greatest. Since you are not concerned with exposing film, the F-stop number is not critical. You only adjust lens openings to make a more pleasing picture. Since light can so often be controlled, F-stops can be set nearly anywhere you need to set them, in most situations.

The change in depth of field can be observed by framing two objects that are different distances from the camera. When you zoom in and focus on one object, the other will most likely be out of focus. However, as you zoom out, both objects will soon be in focus.

The only time you can focus accurately is when you are zoomed in all the way, on your tightest shot. When zoomed-in fully, the lens has its smallest depth of field. You can then focus precisely. When the lens is at a wide-angle position, the focus ring can be changed quite radically, and little or no difference will be seen on the screen.

It cannot be emphasized too much that a zoom lens can be used wrongly and destroy an effect you are trying to produce. Constant and fast zooming, unless specifically desired, can cause an upsetting feeling in the viewer's stomach. A zoom lens is a fine piece of equipment because it offers the electrographer an infinite variety of focal lengths from which to choose. It can also simulate movement to some extent. But this simulated movement is all too often overused, and is rarely used effectively.

In one production in which I was involved, the infamous picture of Jack Ruby shooting Lee Harvey Oswald in the Dallas police station was on the screen. The director started with a close-up of Ruby's hand on the gun. He then slowly zoomed out to a long shot of the entire scene. Then, as the background music built up in intensity, the cameraman began to zoom in and out wildly. This produced a queasy feeling in the viewer and was exactly the mood and feeling the director had in mind. This was a good use of the medium, to produce a physiological affect on the viewer with simple video and audio signals.

92

CHAPTER 11

HOW TO USE SLOW MOTION, FAST MOTION, STOP ACTION, AND REVERSE MOTION

Slow motion, fast motion, and stop action are video techniques that could be used more frequently and more effectively than they are now. One sees slow motion most often during the football season. The sports shows use this effect very well. They use it to show how the fullback broke through a hole which the linemen opened just in time. Avid sportsfans have been conditioned to expect the "instant replay." They see the action once at normal speed, or in "real time"; then they watch the play a number of times in slow motion. All too often, however, the viewer is caught up in the play—in the maneuvers, rather than in the beauty of the athlete's movements. In slow motion, the smallest details that make a great athlete become obvious to the viewer. One can watch the darting of the eyes, the subtle, supple smoothness of the head and body fakes, and the power of a good runner's powerful long strides.

Only recently have people begun to see the beauty in a sport as violent as football. After having been introduced to the grace of sports in slow motion via video, the mass audience readily accepted the many films that were made about sports in slow motion. The most effective of these that I have seen, in terms of gaining an audience for a new concept, used close-ups, in slow motion, of the action in a championship game. The soundtrack was a well-known ballet. The film was powerful, and had quite an impact. This type of thing could be done easily and inexpensively for a very entertaining and elegant video production. It would be an excellent use of the medium as well. One could shoot the game on a Rover, bring it back to a deck with slow motion capability (nearly all have it), and put in the music while dubbing the video, in slow motion, to another deck, or even back to the Rover, if there is no other deck.

Industry has been using slow-motion video for years. On an automated high-speed manufacturing assembly line, there is no way anyone can actually watch the processes to determine whether everything is running correctly. Companies used to use film, but there was always the delay, of course, for the processing, and they also couldn't get a very detailed super-slow image. Now, however, using modified vtr's, they can get incredibly slow, accurate, and detailed immediate results.

Slow motion has been used very effectively by educators. They use it to teach students any repetitive motor function, from hitting a baseball, to proper lip movement with students who have difficulty in pronouncing words, to improving a marching band's coordination.

Dramatic uses of slow motion video tape have not been very extensive. However, there is beginning to be a increase in tape as opposed to film production on the networks, and now that television is getting back to video, and keeping the medium pure, we can expect to see more use of slow motion as a dramatic form. There is no reason why we, as portable electrographers, can't use it, however. Slow motion is usually used to portray dream sequences, and this is what the viewer has been conditioned to expect when things slow down.

Television, as a *real-time* medium, unlike film which is dream-like anyway, has not yet fully explored the possibilities of changing the viewer's time sense (see Chapter 12). If you are planning on doing a dramatic tape, and a scene calls for an important series of events, in which each movement is essential to the story line, try the scene in slow motion. Tape it, then slow it down. If every movement forces the viewer to carefully observe what takes place, and impresses upon him the intricacies of the action, without noticeable disturbance of his time sense, then use the scene in slow motion; you can quickly tell whether it will work or not, just by viewing it yourself. If it doesn't work slowed down, then just use it at normal speed.

94

How to Use Slow, Fast, Stop, and Reverse Motion

Slow motion video is an inherent use of the medium. It is simple, and nothing special must be accounted for. In film, they must run the stock through the camera at a very high rate of speed, so that it will appear to be slow motion when played back at normal speed. They must also make a compensation in the F-stop, and then adjust the lighting, etc. Since *motion* is recorded smoothly on a video tape recorder, and not in interrupted bits, as in film, any adjustment of that motion is easy. On the newer vtr's, even on the least expensive ones, a slow-motion mode is standard equipment. To do a scene in slow motion, you need only two machines, and only one of those need have slow motion capabilities. Tape the scene on the machine with it, then play it back in slow motion while dubbing the slowed tape to the other machine. No special lighting, no jiggling with F-stops, and very little preplanning is needed. All you really need is the imagination and creativity it takes to see an opportunity that calls for a distortion of time, and to use the proper technique to bring it off.

Fast motion is a little more difficult to do. To my knowledge, there is no machine, in the industrial or institutional price range, that has a fast-motion mode. With practice, however, you can achieve moderately acceptable fast-motion results. Simply put the machine into fast forward and rest your thumb on the supply reel, applying a slight amount of pressure. By watching the monitor and varying the pressure, you will see that you can maintain a relatively steady rate of speed. Once again, this requires a second vtr, as you must dub the speeded-up tape to the other recording machine. The whole trick is to keep the machine, via your thumb pressure, just below the speed where the picture breaks up, as it does in fast forward and rewind.

Broadcast television has a device that has not only slow and fast motion, and stop action, but reverse motion as well. The machine records on a magnetic disk, instead of tape, and has only about a thirty-second recording time capability. This is the device they use for instant replay at sporting events. The disk rotates as the head moves over it. By moving the video head, the operator has absolute control over which portion of the sequence goes out. He can move the head in such a way as to play back super-slow motion, and stop the action at any one field, and hold it there as long as needed. For fast motion, the machine is set to play back only every other field. This creates action that moves at twice the normal speed, with nearly indiscernible flutter. It can also go from slow motion to fast motion to fast reverse, instantly, which can create highly amusing results. The machine has highly restrictive functions, however, that make it usable only for certain applications. The thirty-second capacity is one, another is the fact that there is no audio recording provision, and the price tag of $35,000. All of these factors contribute to keeping this type of equipment out of our hands, for the moment.

Fast motion deserves some comment. When we run a tape for people who don't have a lot of exposure to vtr's, we've noticed an interesting phenomenon. Most people begin to laugh as the tape speeds up, going into fast forward, just before you lose the image, where you can still see the characters on the tape speeding around. What's so funny about these images racing about the screen? More often than not, the tape itself is not a humorous one. In Kirk Smallman's excellent book *Creative Film-Making*, he believes, as do I, that people have become conditioned to think of a speeded-up scene as funny. In the old silent comedies, fast motion was the way they made things seem ridiculous. They could also pull off seemingly hazardous stunts, without danger to the actors. There is no doubt that inserting a segment of speeded-up motion into an otherwise real-time sequence, will call attention to the speeded-up one, and will make that portion seem silly. Using fast action for making fun of something has become somewhat of a cliché, since you can manipulate the viewer into a humorous frame of reference. This peculiar frame of reference probably comes about because all actions, such as running, falling, jumping, walking, gesturing, etc., are finished before anyone can get involved with the action. Slow motion, on the other hand, has an opposite effect. Slowing things down increases the dramatic effect, since it allows the viewer time to see and feel everything that happens; it allows him to empathize with the action taking place on the screen. It would seem that when the time of a segment is slowed down, the viewer can become involved with an infinite number of details and emotions, and can experience numerous emotional changes. When time is speeded up, however, the viewer tends to detach himself emotionally from the scene, and watch only the patterns of the action, which more often than not, strike him as being funny.

Stop action has some interesting uses. Many machines have stop-action capability. Even the Rover can stop the tape movement and keep scanning, continuously replaying the same field. It is used basically in sportscasting, industry, and education to show one instant of an action, to teach just how that instant came to be, and the correctness or mistake involved. Stop action offers more to the electrographer looking for different and unique ways to present his material. We have frozen action during editing for a very nice effect. You can begin a series of segments with a freeze-frame, then let the tape go on running at normal speed until the last shot of that segment, then freeze that. Now cut to a stopped shot of the next segment, and then let it run until the last shot, and then freeze that, and so on, throughout your tape. This creates continuity, gives you good reference points for your edits, and makes pleasing transitions throughout the sequence.

There are some interesting things you can do with stop action in dramatic and documentary tapes, as well as in the instructional ones. If you have an off-screen narrator, sometimes it is beneficial, when you get to an intriguing scene, to freeze the tape, and let the narrator's voice continue on, dubbed in over the scene. This allows the viewer time to listen to the narration and carefully observe all there is to see in that scene. It doesn't always have to be an interesting visual point you want to get across; the audio might be important enough to stop the video, so let the audio go with no distractions.

These are a few ideas of how you can use stop action, or freeze-frames. Once again, since portable video is such a new medium, it will be up to you, the electrographer, to devise new uses for the inherent features already available to us.

One of these new uses is reverse motion. As far as broadcast television is concerned, the only way to get a tape to play in reverse, is to use a disk recorder. This is not the case, however. It can be done, it just takes practice and time. The mechanics of reverse motion are tricky, since it can't be done electronically as yet (but I'm sure it won't be long before it can). Carefully plan the scene you'd like to do in reverse. Then, preferably on a tripod, tape the segment with the camera held upside down. This is difficult, but it can be worked out. If the scene requires much camera movement, forget the tripod, since it will become very confusing. With practice, you will find that shooting with the camera upside down can become quite smooth.

Since the portion of tape that has the reverse motion segment on it must be physically cut off the reel, always start taping at the beginning of a reel. You could do it in the middle of a reel, but by the time you get back to it, or try splicing it in the field, you'll wish you had planned ahead. Once you have taped the scene upside down, cut the tape as close to the end of the scene as you can, and you are ready to splice. Using splicing tape made specifically for video tape, carefully keeping the recording side facing you, reverse the tape.

A physical edit will appear as a wipe from the top or bottom of the screen. Before you make the first cut in the tape, dab some "Edivue," or other tape developer on the edge of the tape. This makes the control pulses visible. The pulses are spaced ½" apart and you should make your cut right on the pulse mark, on both pieces of tape to be spliced. You must line them up quite precisely.

Then, splice what had been the end of the segment that you taped upside down, to the end of the segment that will play back just ahead of it in the finished tape. Next, splice the beginning of the upside-down tape to the start of the following scene. This may sound a bit confusing, but once you try it out, you will see that it is actually quite obvious. Since you taped the scene upside down and forward, when you reverse the tape and invert it, you get a right-side-up tape that plays back in reverse.

Now that you've gone to all the trouble of learning how to get a reverse motion video tape, some discussion of its uses is called for. Reverse motion has hardly ever been used creatively. Used mostly just in comedies, it has virtually never been used at all in video. Some obvious things that can be done are funny little sketches where shattered windows magically reassemble themselves, or fires miraculously put themselves out and undo the damage they have done.

An important thing to remember is that quite often when something is reversed, it is no longer the same action, in reverse. It may be an entirely different type of forward action. Imagine making a tape about an alien culture that is remarkably like ours, but has very subtle differences. In this science fiction tape, the hero may have gone through a space warp, let's say, and landed on what he thought was Earth. However, little peculiarities upset him. For example, baseball players throw with their gloved hands, and catch with their bare hands. They like their lawns long and messy, except that the grass grows short and evenly, so they have machines that mess up the lawns as the machine passes over the grass. Also, these people use a device that looks like a cigarette to draw smoke out of their lungs. This can go on until you run out of ideas. All these things

98

are easy to do, just reverse the action on the baseball players and the smokers. The lawn mower would be just a little harder. All you have to do is have the person cutting the grass walk backward with the mower, so when you play it back, after shooting it upside down, he will appear to be moving forward.

Having people move backward, and then presenting that in reverse motion, offers some interesting actions. Although it seems to be correct, and is going in the right direction, the motion is jerky and not very smooth, and the action will be unnatural. Taping things in this manner will allow you to visually show the emotions of people who approach situations that they are hesitant about, ones that they would rather retreat from than approach.

Slow and fast motion, stop action, and reverse motion, are all ways of distorting the viewer's frame of reference, and time sense. They must be used with care and planning, or they won't work at all. Used well, however, they are powerful means to a creative end —the production of a valuable tape.

CHAPTER 12

SHOOTING FOR SPACE AND TIME

Controlling the rate of time flow on video tape is a difficult and time-consuming effort. However, it is an extremely powerful use of the medium. Powerful because of one very important psychological aspect of the medium. Television is a *real-time* medium. In other words, when watching television, the viewer has the feeling that what he is seeing is actually taking place, right now, in front of the cameras. Television is real. Most of what people see on the tube is either "live" or "live on tape"; anything else is, obviously, film.

The average viewer probably could not say whether he is watching video tape or film, but he does *feel* the difference. There are very definite reasons for this. Film is meant to be projected, larger than life, on a bright screen, to a darkened room full of people, not speaking to one another. It is shown in an unreal environment, an unfamiliar one, where the audience has no control over the audio, video, or room temperature, and they must pay for snacks. Television, on the other hand, is quite different in every way. TV is not meant to be projected (and when it is, it loses a good deal of impact); it is viewed in a room that is bright, in an informal atmosphere. People talk to one another, walk around, and have total control over the environment, because it's usually their own home.

More importantly, television is an environmental concept. In *Guerrilla Television,* Michael Shamberg points out that it would be hard to imagine a film left on in someone's living room, which is just what happens with TV. People turn on their set, many times, just to keep from feeling lonely. As soon as their house gets filled up with sound, they walk away, and are only subliminally aware of the programming flowing from the set.

Television and film differ greatly in the nature of their images. A film is only the projected shadow of a light passing through a strip of plastic. It appears as flat as the plastic from which the image came. A television image is made up of light coming from an object, and being scanned by an electron beam, it is played back the same exact way it was recorded, on the same piece of tape, unlike film where the final product is usually at least two generations removed from the original. Film is literally an illusion. In any motion picture, nothing is shot in "real time." Even a conversation between two people is faked. A scene of two people talking is usually shot three times. Once, it is done as a long shot in one continuous take, of the whole conversation, showing both participants; then it is shot again showing one person talking and reacting; and the third take is of the second person talking and reacting to the first. These three takes, of scenes that may have been shot weeks apart, are then edited together to give an illusion of a real-time conversation. (*Real time* means that if it takes a girl two minutes to walk across a beach to the water, it also takes her two minutes to do it on the screen. By means of cutaway shots, and other editing tricks, an editor can make the trip much longer or shorter, depending on the purpose of the scene.)

Since people are aware of the illusionary aspects of film, they more readily accept tampered time in film. However, since television is so very real, when things don't happen in a "real-time" order, the viewer is thrown off. Film makers have to shoot in that way because of the nature of their medium. However, with two cameras running simultaneously, with no possibility of waste, a television program is shot all in one take, and nobody would assume that it should be done any other way.

When it is decided to shoot in such a way that time is expanded or contracted, one must work with the knowledge that, unless the shooting and editing go well, this playing with the viewer's time sense will not go unnoticed.

To discuss this concept of distorting time, let us take the example of the girl walking across the beach. She is quite beautiful, and has a striking figure, which is enhanced by her brief bikini. As she walks by some men playing football on the sand, the quarterback becomes so distracted that he is easily tackled by an opposing player, and is thrown into the water. In "real time" this scene may have taken less than 10 seconds, not long enough to fully develop into a worthwhile scene. The problem is, how to expand the time, without confusing the viewer.

The first shot of the scene would have a long shot of the boys playing ball. One at a time, the team facing the camera notices the girl as she enters the frame from the left. Cut to a medium shot of the girl strolling toward the camera. Cut to a close-up of the individual team members following her with their eyes. A CU of the girl. Cut to a medium shot of the quarterback as he sees her for the first time, then, a slow zoom-in to a close-up of the quarterback. Cut to a long shot of both teams and girl, the team with their backs to the camera doesn't see her, and neither does the center of the team with the ball. He hikes to the quarterback, who is oblivious, as are all his teammates, except the center. Cut to a long shot from the side as the other team rushes in and throws the quarterback into the ocean. Cut to a long shot of the tangle of boys, and the girl innocently reaching the water and testing it with her toe.

We have taken a simple sequence, and by enlarging on all the individual segments that make up the whole scene, we expanded the actual "real time" of this scene, and made it twice as long. One of the reasons why we do expand real time occasionally is to let the audience become much more a part of the action. By expanding and showing all the little nuances that go on during a real-life situation, the viewer becomes more aware of the mood and meaning that you are trying to portray. He can anticipate and understand the scene better. He will hardly ever realize that time has been expanded to allow him this insight.

In all probability, you will more likely want to shorten the time of an action than to lengthen it. When preparing a tape on any subject, there are usually some aspects of that subject that are repetitious, noninformative, and visually unappealing. The simplest way to avoid these portions of your tape is to just not shoot them. For example, if in a tape you are making, someone is digging a ditch, you need not waste 15 minutes of tape showing every shovelful. Show the first few and the last few; people will get the idea.

Another way to compress time is to use cutaway shots. A cutaway shot can always take less time than the shot it replaces. Had we wanted to get that girl quickly across the beach, in less than the 10 seconds that it really did take to walk that far, we could have done this: long shot of the girl walking across the beach; cut to medium shot of boys watching her; cut back to medium shot of girl reaching water and testing it with her toe. This sequence of shots may have only taken 5 seconds instead of 10. It's all done in the editing. You should shoot the entire sequence of the girl walking down to the water. Then, when you are ready to edit, show her walking for the first few seconds, insert the cutaway shot of the boys watching, advance your master tape to the last few seconds of her walk, and add that. The missing few seconds will never be noticed by the viewer, and they made the pace of your scene quicker.

Cutaways are the easiest, and best, method of compacting time. However, they are not always necessary. If you are showing any repetitious action, especially in an instructional tape, you can use a jump cut. A *jump cut* is when you remove the middle part of an action. Had we not cut away to the boys watching the girl stroll to the water, the action would have "jumped" unnaturally. If, however, you are taping a demonstration of how to cut metal with a hacksaw, for example, there is no need to show the entire cutting process. It is quite acceptable to show only the first few starting saw strokes, cut to a few seconds about half way through, and then cut to the final strokes as the cut piece falls away. The viewer may or may not realize that you took him through a lengthy operation rather quickly, but even if he does, it will not interfere with the information you are presenting to him.

Jump cuts may also be used for an effect on the viewer in a dramatically oriented tape. You need some good editing gear, but if you have it, and have the patience to make twenty or so cuts in a minute of tape, it is very effective. Imagine what it is like to watch some action, continually jumping, sporadically into the future. It thoroughly upsets one's time sense, and should be used sparingly, but when needed.

If you've got a switcher/fader, a series of slow dissolves has always been an effective way of distorting time. Assuming you don't want to upset the viewer's time sense, but you do want to get the hero of the story out of the city to see his girlfriend in the country, you obviously can't have an hour of scenes of him driving along the highway. It also might be difficult to get good tape of all the driving scenes. A simple solution might be to shoot some stills, or even cut pictures out of magazines of highways scenes, and slowly dissolve from still to still, and then cut to the hero arriving at his girlfriend's place. This technique will work well, it will save you a good deal of time, and it will not adversely affect your production. Now, this will work well only in a dramatic type of presentation, although if you are doing a factual, documenting type of program, you can use authentic photographs of the actual journey that took place. However, this will involve more risk in that the viewer may not be prepared to accept this type of technique in a program that is not dramatic. If you don't overdo it, these dissolves will work fine.

Another easy and effective way to make time pass more quickly, is to use the purely optical effect of going in and out of focus. To compress time, slowly go out of focus in the last scene of the first segment involved. The focusing will work much better if you end the scene in a tight close-up. (The reason is clear, if you've read Chapter 8.) Then, jump cut to the next scene, but have that scene start widely out of focus. If you can, all effort should be made to have the two scenes equally as blurry, so as to make the transition as smooth as possible. If you are going to start altering people's time sense, you ought to go about it in as smooth and pleasant a way as possible. The second segment will be as advanced as you want it, but the focusing business will be readily accepted. This is an extremely easy effect to achieve with Porta-Paks, since the edits they make when you pull the trigger are clean enough so as to make the middle of the focus part, where you actually change scenes, nearly invisible.

Do not overdo this particular technique, however, since it can become painful to watch after only a very few applications. A true sign of an inexperienced cameraman or director is the overuse of a pretty device. You can make it not only not pretty, but downright annoying. I can't stress this point enough. A straight show, with no gimmicks or special effects, is much better than a program that has even one poorly used or out-of-place effect. Be cautious, and use these devices only if they themselves demand to be used. After a while, you will learn to "hear" the tape itself call for a particular effect. When you can realize this, then it will be unlikely that you will incorrectly use an effect.

104

Shooting for Space and Time

The use of this in-and-out of focus will work quite well, because it is used so often in commercial video and in film. There is no reason to not take advantage of reactions that commercial interests have built into the viewing audience. The broadcasters have trained their audiences to expect certain things when certain devices are used. Since this conditioning already exists in the visually literate viewer, take advantage of it. Networks may have programmed their audiences in this manner to sell soap, but the conditioning is there for you to use as well. Use it to sell ideas, concepts, and beauty. Use it even to teach people how to become more visually literate, and even to teach them that they have become conditioned, so conditioned in fact that we not only recognize the conditioning, but use it at our will!

As for shooting for space and time, some neat devices have been discussed here for changing the time flow of your production, and for altering the time sense of your audience. Television *is* a real-time medium, and depending upon how well you understand this, and how well you use the techniques, this changing of time can be very powerful and effective, or it can destroy any flow your production may have had. Because of the unique nature of our medium, however, it usually works superbly. It's certainly worth a try.

CHAPTER 13

VIDEO ANIMATION

Video animation is difficult and time-consuming. When well done, however, the effects are startling. Due to the real-time and reality orientation of video, and because people are not accustomed to seeing video animation, the latter produces interesting viewer reaction. Whenever we've shown animated tapes, the viewer's most common reaction is, "I think I missed something; could I see that again?" He doesn't believe what he has seen. It is as if something, or someone, disappeared before his very eyes, which is, of course, exactly what has happened.

People are very aware of the illusionary aspects of film. When they watch an animated film, having been indoctrinated at an early age by Walt Disney, they can accept that for what it is, an imaginary or fantasy world created for their entertainment. Animation was a new medium, totally unlike film. At first, people just assumed that it was another kind of "movie." If you recall, one of the basic rules of media, is that when a new medium comes along, it is thought of as a new adaptation of an old, or already existing, medium. It really wasn't until Disney and Warner Brothers (remember "W-W-W-What's up, Doc?") began to make feature-length "cartoons" that people began to think of animation as not only a new medium, but a new tool. Educational film producers, teachers, and scientists got together and realized that things they could only describe or show still pictures of, could be shown accurately, and quite clearly, using an animated film. The most prevalent use of this type of educational animation in use today, is the way the networks use it during the flights to the moon. We watch the rocket stages separate, and the vehicle land on the moon. The animation is so precise that what we watch on film is actually taking place, at exactly that moment. Of course, one of the nicest things about film animation, is that since it is a frame-by-frame process, timing can be absolutely perfect, down to $\frac{1}{24}$ of a second, since that is how many frames are shown per second, at sound film speed.

Unfortunately, the laborious process that makes film animation so smooth and accurate, is now helping to kill off this medium, in a creative sense. An artist must draw every movement seen on the screen, frame by frame. In the Disney classics, such as *Bambi* or *Snow White,* it took a large staff of artists years to complete the films. This may seem incredible, but think about the fact that not only are there 24 separate drawings, or "cells" as they are called, per second for each of Snow White's movements, but the perspective of the background must constantly be changing as well. Therefore, there are 1,440 frames per minute of film!

The Disney studio also did a number of overlays in each scene to give the film more of a three-dimensional look. If you can imagine the fabulous expense this was back then, you must begin to realize why the production of full-length, and even short, animated films has slowed down considerably. You can see the difference in quality by watching the Saturday morning children's shows. About the only thing that actually moves in these new cartoons, is the characters' mouths. Everything else remains motionless. Such is the state of the economy's effect on art.

Two feature-length animated films appeared recently, and they deserve some comment, because of the technique and concepts involved. *Yellow Submarine* was truly a fantasy trip. The creators of this film knew that they had a guaranteed hit, since they were cashing in on the popularity of the Beatles. They could get a good deal of financial backing, and they probably could have done a Disney kind of thing. But today, with our heightened media awareness, a Disney fantasy is about as much a fantasy as a Norman Rockwell painting. Animation finally came into its own, when people began to realize that a fantasy medium cannot succeed if it tries to imitate real life.

Making the Media Revolution

The "Yellow Submarine" people knew this and used a new sort of animation, a kind that had begun to be used in low-budget films. Since they had the money, however, they could afford to dress it up and make it work beautifully. Put simply, this technique allows the camera to run at normal speed for much of the film. While the camera is running, the background, foreground, or characters, or all three, are physically moved, eliminating the individual cell concept. Of course, they couldn't do this throughout the film, but often enough to change the mass audience's conception of animation, even if only slightly.

Fritz, the Cat, on the other hand, had a good deal more traditional animation in it, but still deserves some comment concerning the way in which it changed the mass audience's conceptual view of cartoons. Fritz and his friends were drawn in the traditional way, but the backgrounds were highly stylized, and there was a good deal of camera movement around them; in other words, much of the animation came about by moving the camera, not the cells. I felt the most important aspect of "Fritz" was that the "Snow White" image of animated features may finally have been destroyed. In the good old American way, Fritz was the downfall of Snow White's innocence. Entirely new avenues have been opened to the animator: politics, sex, social comment, and social satire. Let us hope that "Fritz's" X-rating will not be the last to be given to an animated cartoon.

I feel that this discussion of film animation is necessary so that you can get a feeling for how different video animation really is, and will be, once you acquaint the mass audience to it. Since there are no frames on video tape, and since you can't possibly make thirty edits per second, you must rethink your concept of animation technique. Electronic editors on broadcast vtr's have this capability, but it's unlikely that the networks will produce any video animation on their machines. It's also unlikely that you will ever get to use equipment like this, so any discussion of what broadcasters could be doing, and what you would do if only you had that equipment, is beyond our realm of possibility. Until computer animation is perfected, there will be very few animated video features.

Computer graphics are not remotely far off in the future. The technique is being refined right now. Basically, what will happen is that you will program the computer with information concerning the movement that you want to take place. Then, with a light pen

108

(a pen that emits a beam of light, as opposed to a pen that's not heavy) an artist can draw the scenes he wants to take place on a light-sensitive cathode ray screen, and the computer will take care of filling in the action from point to point. Since the image is inherently electronic, there is no problem putting the complete work onto tape. (It is imperative that you realize that the future of video is inexorably united with computers. The modes of operation of the two systems are the same, the only difference being that the computer is a print-oriented retrieval system, and video tape is a visually-oriented retrieval system.) Once again, however, we are dealing with a system that at the moment is priced out of our hands, and will not be available to us for a while.

Let us now deal with video animation that is possible to do with portable and inexpensive equipment. If you have a machine with a good electronic editor, and even inexpensive half-inch machines come with them now, you can do simple animation the easy way. The simplest type of thing you can do is to animate real objects. You can make people or objects move about; the only limit is your imagination and patience.

To make a pen magically move across the screen by itself, across a table top, for example, tape about 20 seconds of an empty table top. Then, rewind the tape to the beginning, and move the pen onto the table, so that the tip begins to appear at the edge of the screen. You must rewind the tape at least 15 seconds each time, before you make the next edit, since that's how long the average machine takes to get up to speed. As soon as the empty table top comes onto the screen, hit the edit button and record for another few seconds. Rewind the tape again and move the pen a little farther along its path. This time, as soon as you see the pen appear, hit edit and record for a few seconds. Once again, rewind the tape about 20 seconds and move the pen. Now you will see in rapid sequence an empty table, then the pen appears and moves a little, just as you see it move, hit edit, and repeat this process until the pen has made its journey across the table. It is tedious, but when you play back the completed tape for the first time, you will be delightfully surprised. You'll see just how startling fantasy-oriented animation looks on reality-oriented video tape.

One successful experiment like this should give you enough impetus to begin trying as many ideas as you can come up with.

Moving people around is another form of live animation. Instead of a pen, have a person take small steps across a road, and use the same technique as with the pen. He will appear to move quickly across the road without moving his feet. Try it, it's fun!

Other, simpler forms of animation are used with graphics. The simplest of all involves having lettering, a title, for example, appear letter by letter. All you have to do is to design the graphic, put it on a stand, and place a black card over it, so that the lettering is completely covered. Then, slowly pull the black card across the title card, from left to right, uncovering one letter at a time. If you have a mixer, this works very nicely supered over a scene that the graphic relates to.

Another very similar technique is to make a strip that has lettering on it, and pull the strip through a card that has two slots in it. Place the lead edge of the strip through the slot on the right-hand side of the card, making sure that there is enough leader on the strip so that your hand doesn't show, and then thread the strip through the slot on the left-hand side of the card. When you pull the lettered strip, the title will move in front of the camera from right to left. This same technique can be used to make graphs move up and down, and to have the temperature rise in a thermometer.

Another way to show movement along paths of a graphic is to cut a slot, an inch or two thick, into the graphic, and cover the slot with some opaque tape. As the need arises to show more and more of the movement of whatever you are trying to show, just peel off that portion of tape from behind.

Something that is a little more involved, but produces interesting images, involves buying a ferrotype plate from a camera store. A ferrotype plate is a very shiny, thin piece of metal, which can be bent and twisted. It can be used to reflect an image onto a rear screen device, or onto any reflective surface. Design your title or whatever image you have in mind, and transfer it onto a piece of black construction paper that is large enough to cover the metal plate. Next, cut the design out of the construction paper. Turn the paper over, so that you have a reverse image, and glue it to the ferrotype plate. When you shine a bright directional light onto the face of the plate, the shiny portions of the plate will reflect your image onto the screen. If you are using an RP screen, you don't have to reverse the silhouette before gluing it to the plate, since

110

you will be viewing a reversed image through the front of the screen. Once you have that lined up, you can begin to twist the plate around. The more you twist, the more distorted the image becomes. (Herbert Zettl goes into more detail about these processes in his book, *Television Production Handbook.*)

One of the nicest forms of video animation, is moving the camera across still pictures. This technique is discussed in detail in Chapter 9. A combination of this type of camera movement, with some of the editing techniques discussed earlier in this chapter, will produce some very effective results.

Video animation is quite new to the medium, so new, in fact, that maybe we are making the most common mistake of all. Very possibly, when animation becomes more usable, and more used, we will see that it is not just another use of the television medium, but a new medium in itself.

CHAPTER 14

DIRECTING WITH VIDEO TAPE— THE DIRECTOR'S DREAM

Directing ... That's All!

On New York City's Lower East Side, there is a preponderance of superb delicatessens. Most have signs in their windows proclaiming the delights that may be found inside. Signs such as: "Send a Salami to Your Boy in the Army"; "If It's Not Hebrew National, Then Forget It"; "Try Our Hot Knishes"; "Let a Pickle Make Your Day"; and the omnipresent "Let us Cater Your Next Party." Needless to say, there are lots of deli's, and each has its own loyal band of steady customers. The competition between them is fierce, however, and each, through the smells they fan out into the street, and the multitude of signs in the windows, try to lure as many new customers away from the competition as they can. One deli on Houston Street, however, has the Kosher food business about wrapped up. Katz's restaurant is clearly the leader, due mainly to the fact that it really is about the best, and also because the countermen are the best insult artists in the city. (In New York, you see, not only is the food spicy, but so is the way they serve it to you.) The sharp-tongued employees are another reason for Katz's popularity; the best is the best, and people come to enjoy the show.

At any rate, Katz's is so well known, they feel somewhat removed from the need to compete in the window-sign war. Being the consummate delicatessen they are, knowing exactly who they are and what they want, and being the epitome of their medium, their sign merely reads, "Katz's . . . That's All!"

As in the Lower East Side deli competition, so it is in television. If you really know and love the medium, there is only one way to work on a production. There is only one position really worth attaining. To be a director is to be the consummate video connoisseur. It is the epitome of our medium. The finished tape is your doing, from beginning to end. To control and shape the action and flow that goes on before the camera, in a setup anywhere from a single Porta-Pak to a five-camera color studio, has to be one of the greatest thrills one can experience. The pain and satisfaction of watching a tape played back that you created, can really be understood only when one realizes the total involvement that the director has with a tape.

Watching your crew flow around the action that you are taping, not interfering, yet not uninvolved, brings on a certain oneness with that action. This oneness extends not only to the action on the screen, but to the crew members themselves. Most crews that work together all the time in video, form very close ties with one another, and this produces even more smoothly flowing productions.

I don't want to give the impression that I think the other people on a production team are any less important to that production's successful completion, because I fully know how integral they are. If you love the medium so much that you can become emotional when discussing it, or when trying to explain it to visually illiterate people, then you can understand what I am attempting to say. Any involvement in a production—cameraman, audio, lighting, editor, etc.—is thoroughly enjoyable and rewarding. What I'm trying to point out, however, is that directing is the cat's meow of video . . . That's All!

A director has a particularly hard job, since he must make a highly technical medium work creatively and artistically. If you are a one-man operation, you will run into few personnel problems. If there are more than one of you, as is most likely the case, you as director must get everything you can out of your crew without running into personality and internal political problems. We must assume that the other people on the crew are working at their positions because that's what they do best, or else what are they doing there at all? Even if they've never worked any video gear at all before, they have their crew positions because somebody thought they would be best at that position. Zettl points out (*TV Prod. Handbook,* p. 418) that as the director you must be able to make your crew work *for* you as well as *with* you. The best director is not the person who can get the best shot, but the one who knows why he got it. He is also not the person who can do everything better than anyone, but the one who knows how to get the best performances out of his crew, and who can coordinate the activities of this group of people into a completed, comprehensive, smoothly flowing television production.

Assuming that you are a visually literate person, it will not be hard for you to adapt to two very important processes. They are picturization and visualization. If you are working from a script, you must change what you read into individual pictures in your mind. This is known as *visualization.* In a sense, you are translating print into video. It is very important that you are able to make this step. Visualization may sound like an easy process. For most people it is not. When you can read a newspaper, a script, or a play, and picture each segment as it would look on the screen, you are there. You must be able to visualize not only from print, but from your thoughts as well. When instead of just thinking generally about a tape you would like to make, you begin to think in terms of the individual shots of that production; when you hear a story and can visualize how you would go about taping that story, you have mastered the important art of visualization.

Picturization, on the other hand, involves taking this string of unrelated visualizations, and putting them together into a cohesive unit. Once you are actually able to think in pictures, you must be able to sort out and select these images, and put them in a sequence that will tell your story. Sometimes, the technique of picturization comes to the novice director before visualization. He can imagine what sort of scenes he is going to use to tell his story, but has a difficult time imagining the individual segments that make up the scenes. He can see the production as a whole, but does not really know how he is going to achieve certain effects and moods. It is of no real consequence which technique you master first, but it is important that you understand the differences between the two.

As the director, it is your responsibility to have properly composed pictures on the screen. If the makeup of your production crew

114

includes a director and a cameraman, then it must be decided who will determine the proper framing and composition. The framing of objects on the screen is often so vital to the story line that an incorrectly set up shot would play back like a poorly spelled word in an English composition. It is important to decide who is going to be responsible for all this. If you do have both a cameraman and a director, then the director should set up each shot carefully with the cameraman. If you are dealing with Porta-Paks, obviously this pre-planning is called for because only the cameraman knows what he has. In a situation where you've put your cameras through a switcher or special effects generator, then the director can watch the shots develop over his monitors, and guide and correct the cameraman as the program goes along.

A detailed discussion of framing and composition is included in Chapter 9, but some additional points are called for here. As everyone knows by now, Marshall McLuhan says that television is a "cool" medium. One of the reasons he sees television as being cool, is that the size of the screen is so small that it limits the amount of action that can take place, and still be comprehended by the viewer. Any action that is extremely violent or large-scale, is not correct for this medium and won't make it on the tube. Examples are such movies as *The Bridge on the River Kwai, The Longest Day,* and *West Side Story.* While you might have personally enjoyed watching these movies on television, it was probably more of a nostalgic experience; you remembered what it was like in the movie theater, on that 20 foot high screen. Find someone who didn't see one of these, or any large-scale film in the theater, and saw it only on the "small screen." They probably wondered what all the fuss was about.

The point of the above information is, simply, that you cannot attempt a large-scale production, with a cast of thousands, because that just won't work on television. You must understand the medium for its strong points and its shortcomings. As a director, it is essential for you to know that the most effective use of television is its close-up ability. The medium works best when called upon to show intense personal drama. This drama does not have to be serious, or even fictional, but it is important that you use it properly.

When dealing with medium shots and close-ups, it is very important to remember that you should not use too close a close-up. In Western society, we all have a certain amount of space around

115

us that cannot be violated by outsiders. When talking to one another, we very rarely get much closer than 2 to 3 feet from the other person in the conversation. When someone does violate this sphere of privacy, our most usual reaction is to back up a little, just far enough to reestablish the proper distance for conversation. When someone comes up to whisper to you, the common reaction is to turn your head aside and present your ear to him. How often do you actually look at a person whispering or talking intimately to you? Most likely only when making love.

Since we Westerners are so distance-conscious, it makes a big difference in the ways we portray one another, whether in oils, photography, film, or on television. The super-tight close-up is generally used only in love-making scenes, or when the director wishes to negatively portray someone. I'm sure you've seen a politician on a talk show, and have been upset, for some reason, about his appearance. Most likely, your reaction stemmed from a deliberate attempt on the director's part to make you feel that way, because he just didn't like the person. Watch for this technique; the same very tight close-up will remain on the screen for a long, long time. The length of the shot, as well as the closeness, will make even the politician's most loyal supporters feel that there is something wrong with him. What's wrong, of course, is that this director had the nerve to intrude within that private sphere. If you don't think this sphere exists, try going up to someone, even a good friend, but not a lover, and talk inches from his face, and then watch him back up. Once you have taken my word for it, or proven it to yourself, keep this technique in mind. It is very handy for villains, real or imagined, whom you want to portray as such.

If you were working with a large photograph—11″ x 14″, for example—you could include in that print twenty or more faces in a group shot, and anyone could easily identify those people. If, on the other hand, you had to show those same twenty people on a television screen, it would be virtually impossible to identify them all. An 18″ screen, roughly the same size as the photograph, just will not portray the same amount of information. People sit farther back from a television screen; even children who notoriously sit very close, only sit as near as they would to a friend, proving just how real and intimate an object people consider television. It is not necessarily intimate to them, but an object with the potential for intimacy.

116

A photograph, on the other hand, is inanimate and can be closely scrutinized for a long period of time, unlike the television image which passes quickly, and cannot remain on the screen for too long a period of time. The average length of a shot in a moderately paced show lasts about 5 seconds. A 10-second shot that does not move is tedious, and a stationary 15- or 20-second shot is unbearable.

Shots can last longer, however. You as the director must allow the action that is taking place to provide enough motion to overcome the fact that there is no camera movement. If you are faced with the prospect of taping someone talking, and you have only one Porta-Pak with which to do it, your only way out is to start with the classical long shot. Then do a slow zoom-in to as tight a close-up as you want, in light of the discussion above, and hold that for a while. Then you can go out to a medium shot, and so on. The best bet is to hold a loose medium shot. As the talk builds in intensity (if, in fact, it ever does), zoom in, as it slows down, zoom out a bit, but match your shooting style to the mood of the talk.

Another reason for McLuhan's label of TV as a "cool" medium is the way in which the medium directs the viewer's attention. When watching a program, the viewer can see only a small part of the total action. Whether watching a parade, a ball game, or a riot, the only thing that reaches the viewer is what the director decides to put on the screen. He is severely limited in this, since he knows that wide-angle shots do not work very well. So he must select what he feels to be representative shots of the entire scene. Not being able to clearly show an entire ball park, or all the events at a demonstration, will not easily allow the real mood of an event to come across. The director must be able to accurately portray the mood of any event by his pacing, framing, and flow.

Television tends to cool things down because of this small frame. If the things portrayed in that frame are small as well, they will be nonexistent for most viewers. The reason why the Chicago police appeared so ruthless (aside from any political considerations) at the Democratic Convention in 1968, was because the nature of the television medium made them appear to be such incredible monsters. They were monsters because they provided so much violent activity in such a concentrated space—your television screen. There is no question that they were overzealous in their pursuit of their duty, but television turned this scene of ignorant, confused men into a

117

scene of brutish animals committing ultraviolence. TV is the true Theater of the Absurd. Anything that doesn't play well on the screen, or just doesn't cut it on this medium, looks ridiculous, absurd. Those cops looked terrible because their kind of action was too violent, too intense, and not at all on a personal level. Their hate was portrayed as against *all* long hairs, and *all* youth. If individual enemies of the police were singled out and beaten, while a network news team got nice close-ups of the scene, the whole riot would have played very well, and maybe our thoughts of that event would be very different. At least the cops would have received more sympathy than they did.

I use Chicago as an example of the power of television to "cool" down, relatively speaking, the events that it portrays. No one can claim that watching those events every evening was pleasant or unemotional. However, had the same events been shown to all of America on color film, in movie theaters, the reaction of the people would have been radically different. There would have been rioting in the streets everywhere. No one could have watched that kind of action, on film, and just felt mad and frustrated, as most of us did. Even the movie *Medium Cool* got people more worked up than the "CBS Evening News" did. People were very upset, to be sure, and outraged, but what happened? Not much. Television really did cool down even the extremes of Chicago.

The people who were sitting in the big TV vans in Chicago were certainly not directing the action outside (although there still seems to be some debate about this) nor were they telling the cameramen what kinds of shots to get. (Can you imagine, "That's it, Camera 2, go in a little bit, there, that's fine, a nice medium two shot of the cop and the hippie.") They allowed the flow of the action to determine their pacing and flow. No one, however, should be able to determine your style. Every director develops his own style of directing. Most styles are similar, since everyone is working with the same basic tools, but people tend to fall into their own unique patterns.

I once worked at a station that had four Producer/Directors on staff. Each of these men had his own way of getting his show done. Most directors anywhere in television fall into the basic categories that these people represented.

The first man had a production conference with the crew before every show. This is usually done in broadcast television, so that no one is surprised with some event during the production of that program. His style was authoritarian. He told every cameraman exactly what shots he would have during every minute of the show, before the show began. You, as cameraman, always had to watch your shot sheet (a list of your shots, usually taped to the rear of the camera) and have the next shot set up as soon as the previous one had been used. There was no improvisation allowed on either the cameraman's part or the director's. This type of directing works very well in very complicated shows, and in fully scripted ones, which already have the shots written in. It is a style that is almost mandatory if the program has a large number of special effects and complicated maneuvers. Everyone on the crew must be well aware of his responsibilities, as well as those of the other crew members, so that the program will function at all. In a very detailed production, the director sometimes just can't worry about getting his cameraman set up; there just may be too many other things happening at once, and if all the camera shots are preplanned, that is one less thing to worry about.

The obvious drawback to this type of directing style is that there is absolutely no room for improvisation, for last-minute changes, or for emergencies. Changes and emergencies can be tolerated of course, but once a crew is used to working under these conditions, things never seem to flow as smoothly if the style is changed. Good directors can change their methods to meet varying program needs. Some people are not capable of this, however, and this style would be a disaster for them.

The next kind of director on staff at the station never handed the cameraman a shot sheet before the show; he just went over with them what areas they were to cover. During a show, he gave very specific commands to them as to what their shots were to be, as the show progressed. There was no improvisation here, either. You always were to hold the previous shot until told to move, and then move only to the shot described by the director. This type of directing allows the director some more freedom and maleability when working the flow and format of a particular show. He can create images, in a series, as the program goes along. The cameramen are always attentive, which is not always the case with the style mentioned first, and so the type of shots during a show can change drastically, as the mood or intensity of the content changes.

The problem with this type of direction is that it forces the director to devote most of his attention to the cameramen, and not to the rest of the production crew. There is no question that what the cameramen display is the most vital aspect of a program, but other production elements warrant much attention as well. The director many times cannot devote himself solely to camera shots and angles.

Another problem with both this style and the one above is that they are very frustrating to the cameraman. He must be made to feel an integral and valuable part of the crew. The cameraman is well aware that a mistake on his part can destroy a show, and he works hard at pleasing the director. Quite often, however, the cameraman feels that he is just an extension of the director's arms. If a director allows no creativity on the cameraman's part, and sets each shot up from the control room, or beforehand with the person operating a Porta-Pak, the cameraman is just an operator, nothing more. This develops ego problems, and should be avoided.

The third director at the station was the opposite of the first two described. He not only never handed out a shot sheet, but he never told you anything. When the cameraman went into the studio (or more often, out of the truck, as this director was used mainly for remote broadcasts), all he heard was, "You can see what's going on out there better than I can; give me the best shots you can, and always be ready to go on the air." This last warning is vital to broadcasters, because many times a cameraman is trying out different shots, or focusing, or just looking around, and if the director puts him on, the viewers get a good look at nothing for a while. Therefore, the admonition to always have a usable shot is an important one.

This director usually did sports, parades, speeches, conventions, and anything else that had no real format. His style perfectly matched the type of shows that he directed as they too were free-flowing and impossible to script. In a free-form atmosphere such as sports or town meetings, the crew must always be as alert as possible. The director has to depend on the cameraman's judgment.

A directing style like this has its place in nonscripted, no-format type programs. It also works best in situations where the cameraman and the director work very closely, and the director has little or no say in what the cameraman is shooting. That is to say, the director is not concerning himself with picture composition and framing; he is primarily concerned with program content, and leaves the

120

shooting entirely up to the cameraman. This type of working arrangement is best suited to the Porta-Pak type situation.

On the other hand, if you have more than one camera going, whether Porta-Paks or through a special effects generator, this style will not do at all. Unfortunately, more often than not all the cameramen will end up with similar shots, if no one gives them specific directions. In a multicamera setup, the director must define every cameraman's shots, or you will end up with a lot of repetitive tape. One of the most frustrating things for a director is to have two or three cameras all on the person who just finished speaking, and no one giving him a shot of the person who just jumped up out of his seat and is shouting a very colorful reply. By the time one of the cameras gets a shot of the person, he has calmed down, and is no longer as visually interesting. The director must exercise the proper control for all the varying situations.

The fourth director at the station was a very nice blend of all of the above. One can't say that he was the best of the four, as each had his own strong points. He was, however, the most versatile, and the most fun to work under. His particular style was to go over the kinds of shots that he expected from each cameraman. He would tell each of them what areas of the set they were to cover, and which persons or group of persons they were to get. Each cameraman knew just what his limits were, so there was very little overlapping and duplication. In fast-moving sequences, he would always have one camera on a long shot, and another on medium and close-ups. This way he never got "hung" or was never at a loss for a shot of the action.

When a director gets "hung," it means that there are no available shots for him to use that show what is actually taking place. If this should happen to you, and it will for sure, there are some things you can do until the situation has cleared up. First, you can cut to a reaction shot. Show someone in the crowd watching the event, and then when you get things straightened out, get back to the action as soon as possible. The viewer might get a little upset, but not noticeably. If you are working with a Porta-Pak, and something causes you to miss the start of some action, tape a little crowd action to edit into that spot when you are putting the show together.

Another way out of a situation where you don't have a shot of the action that is taking place, is to evenly zoom out on the camera that is on the line when you get hung up. This procedure very well may get what you are looking for right into the frame, and if not, it will at least show you where to look to find it. Remember, *When in doubt, zoom out!* It never fails.

These four directorial styles cover the basic types of directing. Whether you become authoritarian, semiauthoritarian, free form, or a combination of all of them is up to you. Try them all, since they each are good for different types of shows. Whichever you are most comfortable with is the way you should most often work.

There are other things to consider when discussing the style of a director. Basically, these are concerned not so much with how the show is actually run, but with the style of the shots a director uses in the course of a show, and the order in which he uses them. Again, there are a finite number of things you can do, as everyone works with the same basic hardware, but it is in putting them together that the differences in directing come out.

Some people are very traditional in that they start programs with a long, or establishing shot, and work their way in to medium and close-up shots. Then, during the show, they use all the standard cuts that are required. This is fine. Many times audiences are put off by fancy shots, or avant garde techniques. You must remember that all the fancy directing you are capable of, really is not going to be noticed by the average viewer. Most people aren't even aware that there is more than one camera in a television studio, if they have ever even thought about it at all. All of the effects that you try to bring about are going to work on your audience only subliminally. They will enjoy and appreciate a program, or dislike it, not for the reasons you may think valid, but for reasons they probably don't understand themselves. So much of television viewing is subconscious, especially when the viewer has no conception of what is involved in putting together a program.

Another style is to have a constant flow of camera movement. This can be very beautiful, but must be used with extreme caution, since constant movement can get the viewers seasick, or at least really turn them off about the content of the show. Careful, slow, and deliberate camera movement is perfect for music, and terrible for discussion. You must fit your style to the content of the show. This cannot be stressed too often. People get very involved with how nice a particular shot looks, and they will use it all the time, whether it fits the content of the program or not. It may be a pretty shot, but

122

if it will not enhance the point that you are trying to get across, don't use it at all. "Always play it straight" should be your motto. Try the moves you think will work out, but don't count on them, unless you know for sure that they will work, or if you are playing to a particularly visually literate audience.

An important thing to remember is that television is a very two-dimensional medium. It is true that video offers more realism than film, psychologically, but there is no getting around the two-dimensionality of the image. As the director, it is up to you to give some three-dimensionality to the scene you are taping. This is accomplished by arranging the objects within the frame to emphasize the foreground, the middle, and the background of each scene. Working with "three-shots" can usually give you something to show. Whether the three include two people and a tree, or whatever the combination may be, use the spacing within a scene to clearly define different areas, especially spatial areas. Good lighting techniques, as discussed in Chapter 7, are about the best way to get spatial relationships across. At the very least, lighting will separate objects from the backgrounds that you are using.

When arranging objects within the frame, it is essential to remember that neither the camera nor the people in the scene will probably remain stationary during a scene. So you must plan all movement appropriately.

As you may know, a good 10 percent of the picture area seen on the viewfinder or camera monitor gets lost when the signal is played back on anything other than a video monitor, or, in other words, on a conventional receiver. This means that you must always take this into consideration when framing objects near the edge of the screen. Use a somewhat looser shot than you normally would, if you think something might get lost in transmission.

Many directors and cameramen draw lines on the viewfinders and video monitors to show them what areas are most often lost. You can do this quite accurately by playing a signal live off your camera or line monitor into a regular receiver. Look closely at the receiver and compare that picture with what you see on your monitor. Place objects near the edge of the screen, and note where they disappear on the receiver. With a black marking pen, draw a line all the way around your screen at the point where the information gets lost on the receiver. This line serves as an important reference point for you, and even though things may look too loose to you on your monitor, if kept within these lines, it will look much better to your audience.

No discussion will take place here about picture composition. We have already talked about it in Chapter 9 on the moving camera, and if you still aren't sure how a picture should be composed, just carefully look at all the comic strips you can. The comic artists have much the same limitations that we have when it comes to composition. Their aspect ratio is similar to ours of 3:4, and they also have to get much three-dimensionality into a very flat medium. The "Marvel" comics are particularly good for their artwork. A "Spider-man" book is a good investment. If someone asks what you are doing with a comic book, tell them to read McLuhan's *Understanding Media,* where he describes the similarities between the comics and television. He goes so far as to state that "the comic cartoon is the clue to understanding the TV image" (p. 151).

These basic discussions of directing have included so far styles and techniques of directing cameras and cameramen, and the varied effects that can be achieved using different techniques. Now let us discuss some ideas on directing not the cameras and what goes on behind them, but the people who move about in front of them.

Most of the people who will appear in your dramatic and documentary tapes will probably not be professional actors. Even if they are familiar with acting, they will surely not be ready for the special skills required when working with video. These skills are certainly not hard to master; it is just that there have been so few dramatic-type tapes made with low-budget equipment. Film actors are accustomed to repeating scenes and dialogue over and over again for the specialized method of film acting. Things are not the same in electrography. The procedures are different, mainly because this medium records sound in sync inherently, unlike film where syncing up peoples' lips with the sound of their voices requires a complicated costly procedure. Working with the people, however, is much the same, since acting calls for a great amount of skill and training which the average nonprofessional just has not acquired. Asking an untrained person to keep up an intense dramatic mood for more than a few minutes is virtually impossible. To call up moods and emotions, at will, and remain in them for the duration of a scene, as well as being convincing in these moods, is something well beyond the competence of an untrained person. There are some little tricks that have been used with success to elicit the proper responses from people who have never undergone professional training.

The easiest way to have people work out well in the roles you need filled, is to use people who really fit the part. Most likely, the persons who appear in your productions will be friends, or friends of friends, classmates, those who heard you were looking for someone to fill a particular part, and people just interested in video. Out of all these people, it shouldn't be too hard to do some typecasting. If your script calls for a street-wise Inner City ghetto dweller, a friend from Scarsdale will not do. If you don't know anyone who fits this description, ask around for the Street Theater nearest you. There are lots of them, and they are always looking for new ways to gain exposure for their members. If no one you know can think of anyone to portray a role in your tape, don't forget about all the amateur theater groups that abound in almost every town and neighborhood.

Once you have the people that you think will be able to spend the time and energy to act in your program, you must reinforce their desire, and give them reason to have confidence in you as an electrographer. Talk to each of them individually. In these discussions tell them about your philosophy of media, and the types of programs you taped in the past. Tell them the people for whom you have already done programs, and what type of groups will most likely be seeing this tape. If you have done a lot of public-service type programs, tell these people about them. If you think this tape has a good chance of being sold to a cassette duplicating company, or to a cable company, be sure to tell them about it. Explain how you intend to split the profits, if any, how the financing will work, and how the credits will read. This is of particular importance if you are working with groups who are eager for exposure. Next, go into some detail about the part you would like them to play. At this point, there are only three responses you will get. They will either be totally uninterested, or flattered and interested, or unsure. If, after your whole pitch about yourself and the proposed program, they show no interest, forget about them. If they are interested, fine. If they are hesitant, however, find out why. You can help in their decision making by explaining about the amount of time that would be required from them, and what they might expect in return.

Many times it will be greatly to your benefit to show some examples of your previous tapes. You must really convince them of your talent and trustworthiness, since you are asking these people to lay out time, and maybe money (buses, gas, dinners, etc.), so that they may have a difficult and demanding job, with the possibility of no financial rewards, just artistic ones.

Once you have finalized the actors, get them together and go over in great detail the story line, and how you envision each of the characters. The actors must have a thorough understanding of their parts before taping actually begins.

The people working on the tape with you are not only interested in seeing themselves on the screen, they are also probably fascinated by television. Since most people are visually literate, or at least have some understanding of what is pleasing to watch on the screen, you should try to involve them in the production as much as possible. Explain the various techniques you intend to use, and such things as camera angles, and special effects. Keep in mind that you are the director, and they must be made aware of this as well, but don't be afraid to take the crew member's and actor's suggestions. You are working with a director's dream medium—video tape! If someone comes up with an idea that may have some merit, shoot the scene that way, then shoot it your way. Look at them both and pick the best; you can't waste tape, only time, and if the suggestion was a good one, you didn't waste any time either.

Even if you think a suggestion is a poor one, and you feel that someone's ego may be hurt if ignored, tape that too. Point out, kindly, why the scene didn't work the way they thought it might, as you watch the playback. You are all in this together, and everyone should have some say in the production.

Don't lose control, however. Very few programs that have been made by committee have been very successful. As the director, you have final say in all matters of artistic judgment. If you have group production meetings, it may help to tape them, and play the tapes back if some sort of a row develops. By all watching the tape together, you will be able to gain insights into one another, as only television can do it. Use the medium personally with your crew, get good interchanges going, and use video all the time. There is no sense in working in video to create some artificial drama about a real-life situation, if you can't use the medium in an actual real-life situation yourself.

Tape is the director's dream, because you can try anything you think might work, and see the results instantly. You can test the actors out and see immediately how they will look in their roles.

126

You don't have to wait as our brother film makers do, to see how a day's shooting worked out. If something didn't work, you know it right away. If you think you might like to try a special effect, try it, you've got nothing to lose. If you don't like the way a scene looks, but the actor can't understand your attitude, play the scene back for him, and point out precisely what it was that you didn't like. Use the inherent, built-in benefits of video tape. Use the tape not only as a device on which to record your images, but as a tool in helping to create those images.

The best, and sometimes the only, way to get untrained actors to portray the proper moods and expressions is to trick them into the responses. If the actor is told to look excited, he may just look silly trying to look excited. You must make him look excited. During the pretaping get-togethers you should try very hard to get to know the personalities of your actors. Once you do know them fairly well, you will know what sort of stimulus on your part will bring on the desired reaction from the actor. Telling a girl that she looks really pretty when she doesn't think that she is being taped, might bring out the perfect happily surprised smile that you were looking for, to be edited into a certain scene.

Catching the actors off guard with carefully planned remarks or actions that you think will elicit certain responses that are just right for certain scenes may sound sneaky. It isn't at all. It is a practice that is often used professionally, and as long as you tell the actor why you did whatever you did, it is excusable. If the actors feel some resentment for being tricked like this, they will feel better about it once you explained why you did it, and how perfect their response was for that scene. When they realize how well they have spontaneously acted, more often than not they will be pleased with their performance.

If a scene calls for someone to walk through a series of actions that are supposed to be unfamiliar to them, and you extensively rehearse the scene, the result will not be at all lifelike. In this type of situation, the best technique to use is to not tell the actor anything about the scene but the barest minimum beforehand. When the scene begins, just tell the actor what he should be doing, or give him hints as to what might be going on. You can dub in the sound later, since all you will be picking up will be comments by the director such as, "Do you see that gun over there? Why don't you see if its loaded? WAIT!! Don't pick it up! It might be booby-trapped. You better run for help!" The audience will see the actor's responses as he looks around for a weapon and then finds the gun. He goes over to the gun, not sure what to do with it, then we see him reach toward it as if to see if it is loaded, then he stops quite suddenly, looks at the gun one more time, and runs out for the police. It all looks natural because it was natural. It was the first time that the actor ever saw the gun, and all his reactions were really spontaneous, since he had never thought of them before. The director knew what he wanted all the time, but couldn't afford to let the actor ham up a scene that had to be played straight and spontaneously.

This technique will work most of the time, but you can't make a constant use of it. The actors don't want to feel that their sole purpose is to be photographic objects moving about in front of the camera, so that the director will have pleasing images to tape. They want to be involved in the making of the tape, and they should be involved as much as possible.

When making documentary tapes, you must avoid the negative power of television to make situations happen just because there is a camera on the scene. Get to know the community or people you will be taping before you actually begin taping there. It's a good idea to show them how a Porta-Pak works, and even let them make some tapes of their own. Show these tapes to the people and explain what your tape will be like. Once they see how simple the whole process is, and how trusting you are, by letting them actually use a television camera, you should have no problems. People are easily won over when you let them use the equipment. Don't be concerned with breakage; someone who has never seen a television camera and who can now use one to tape his family, friends, and street, will probably handle the gear with more care than you do. When they trust you and are familiar with you carrying the equipment around, you will not have difficulty in fading into the background and letting events happen naturally, right in front of your camera.

If you are in a situation where you can't get to know the community beforehand, always be sure to try to play back some of the tape you made on the scene. People are wary of strangers taking their pictures for unknown reasons. If you can show them what you have shot immediately after an event took place, and that you didn't portray them in an unfavorable manner, you are bound to get their cooperation in the future.

There are times, however, when the last thing you want to

128

happen is to have to show the event you just taped to the people who were just involved in it. For example, if you are doing a documentary on garbage removal, and you have just finished taping a truck dumping garbage in an illegal spot, and the driver of that truck, a very large man, wants to know what you are doing with that camera, don't stop the tape! Television cameras are silent, and people generally are not aware of this. If it's not making any noise, they usually assume that the machine is turned off. If you can hold the camera at waist level, and still point it at this guy, you can record what will be a rather damning piece of evidence. "But, sir, what are you so upset about? I was just shooting some scenes for my school play." "Oh yeah? Well, you better get away from here before you shoot some scenes you'll be sorry about!" When playing the tape back, that man's reluctance to be taped will certainly add credence to your story.

Video is the perfect medium for documentary making since it lends itself so well to that type of shooting. You are as portable as can be, and you have to introduce few, if any, artificial devices into the situation, to make it any less real.

To make a truly effective tape, you must rely on a large number of people. You need cameramen, engineers, and actors. You must seek out the people who can help you make the program you have in mind into the most successful production possible. The focal point of any production is the director. The best director is the person who can get the most out of everyone involved in the television process, and do so in the most creative way. It takes hard work and a great deal of knowledge, not only about video techniques and "tricks of the trade," but more importantly, a real understanding of, and feeling for, people. You must know and understand the people you will be directing, before you can hope to control the machines that will do your recording. The technology of television provides you with an excellent way of documenting the events around you, whether in a dramatic or real-life situation. You must be able to direct the actions of people before you can get anything meaningful onto the tape. This can be accomplished only when you are skilled enough in human behavior to get desired responses out of your fellow workers. A director should be not only a good technician, but an understanding, sympathetic, and strong leader as well.

(For a definite account of directing non-actors, read Kirk Smallman's book *Creative Film-Making*.)

CHAPTER 15

EDITING PICTURE AND SOUND

A good clean edit is one where information, either from a live source such as a camera, or from another tape, is added to an already existing tape in a manner that looks as neat as a cut from one camera to another. A good edit is one where you absolutely cannot tell whether the added information came from another source or from a cut to another camera. There are three kinds of editing: *electronic, mechanical,* and *physical.* We will discuss them all.

Electronic editing has always been one of the biggest hangups in electography. Broadcasters never had too much of a problem, because their equipment is so superior electronically. The making of good clean edits was only a matter of function, not a source of headaches, as it is on the one-inch and half-inch video tape recorders. Physical editing is even easier on the quad machines, because the information is put down on the two-inch tape laterally, not diagonally as in helical scan. They can develop the control track and make a straight splice, which in turn becomes a perfect edit. The expensive quad machines do have advantages. You get what you pay for. However, as technology has been advancing at such a rapid rate in helical scan, it is now possible to make perfect electronic edits on the newer half-inch equipment.

As was discussed in the first chapter and in Appendix D, there are parts of the television picture that are not usually seen on a

130

receiver. One of these is the blanking bar, or the vertical interval. The *vertical interval* is the period when the electron gun is turned down and is moving back to the top left-hand side of the raster. There is no picture information here. This bar isn't seen on the screen, except when the set is out of adjustment, when a knob is turned to keep the set from "rolling." The vertical interval is adjusted so that it is put only onto the raster, not the screen. A perfect electronic edit will occur during the vertical interval. In this way, no picture information is disturbed, and the edit will produce no "glitching," which is a highly technical term used to mean picture breakup, and sometimes audio disturbance as well.

Another sign of an unclean edit is very common in edits of all types. The new picture information will appear all right, but it will be accompanied by a "herringbone" pattern on the screen. This pattern of lines will remain on the screen for an agonizing second or two, and there is nothing that you can do to get rid of them, short of making the edit over again.

The original tape that you have made, that is, the one onto which you have recorded all your information first, before any editing or other postproduction alterations have been done, is called the *master,* or *first-generation,* tape. When the information on this tape is transferred to another tape, the next tape is known as *second generation,* and so on, down the generation line. As the information gets farther and farther removed from the original first-generation tape, the quality of the signal deteriorates. Due to this problem, all editing should be done from first-, or at worst second-, generation tapes. For good editing, the signal must be as strong as possible. If you have one available to you, a *video processing amplifier* should be used in the editing procedure. This *proc amp* will ensure that the signal being fed to the editing machine will be a perfect composite signal: .7 volt picture, and .3 volt sync. If your operation calls for extensive amounts of editing, a proc amp should be a mandatory piece of equipment.

There are two types of editing. The first is called *assemble* editing. An assemble edit is the simpler of the two, for all it does is to add information onto already existing information on a tape. An entire tape can be built up by doing a series of assemble edits, adding the scenes as they are to be seen in numerical order. The purpose of assemble editing is to put together in proper order a tape that was shot out of sequence. Any vtr can do assemble editing, even if it does not have a switch on the machine that is labeled "edit." If your machine does not have an edit mode built in, don't let this fool you; you can make edits just as clean as the ones made on machines with cheap editors.

A "cheap" editor is known as a *mechanical* editor. Mechanical editors simply remove the lock that is on the machine to keep you from accidentally recording over tapes that are being played back. No machine will allow you to go from the playback mode directly to the record mode. This is good, since it does save tapes from being destroyed by careless people who might accidentally record right over them. The mechanical edit button simply allows you to deliberately erase old material by lifting the record lock, and thereby adding new material to the tape, in an assemble-edit method. The difference between a mechanical edit and an electronic one is very obvious to the eye. Most often there is a large glitch, accompanied by a very nice display of various herringbone patterns. However, with some practice, people have been known to effect very nice edits, most of the time, with a mechanical editor. The trick to passable edits is to develop a firm, fast button-pushing technique. This may sound ridiculous, but it works, and if all you have available to you is a mechanical editor, you will manage after much practice.

The main drawback to mechanical editors, of course, is that they not only do not operate during the vertical interval, but they have never even heard of it. Therefore, every good edit you get is mainly up to the machine, not you. By developing a rapid, affirmative button-pushing style, you are merely increasing the chances for a good edit, not insuring one.

The way to edit on a machine that has no editing mode, is to record the first scene onto the tape that will become your final or master tape. Then, when you have reached the point where you would like the second scene to start, let the tape run about 10 seconds further on. This will help the vtr lock onto the signal, and also eliminate the chance of having any blank tape if you make the edit a little too late. Then set the second tape up on the other machine about 15 seconds behind the point at which the next scene starts. Next, set the "editing" machine up about 1 second ahead of the spot at which you would like to make your edit. Since it will take the other machine a good 15 seconds to get up to speed, you will have

132

time to get ready. Start that vtr, and set the editing machine in record, and watch its monitor. When it reaches the point where the next scene begins, start up the machine. The secret is to keep the machine in the "ready" mode all the time, by having the heads moving, and the machine in record. You should also keep pressure on the tape by putting your hand on the take-up reel, and making sure that there is no slack in the tape on its path through the head assembly. This way, by keeping the tape taut, when you start the tape transport motor at the point where you want the edit to begin, you should get a good even start. Edits made like this are usually acceptable, and I have seen virtually undetectable ones made. This is a cheap editing process, of course, but by no means a fool-proof one. It will get you through some editing problems if you have no other alternative, but you should not rely on it. Above all, it is very time-consuming, and your desire for a beautifully edited tape will decrease by the hour; in the end, you will be accepting edits that you never would have considered if your patience had not worn so thin.

The present state of the art has made available to us half-inch electronic editing machines that are every bit as good as very expensive one-inch, and even two-inch vtr's. The list price for a ½" color electronic editing tape deck is around $1,600. A few years ago, you couldn't even buy a simple color deck for that. The edits made on this machine are as good as those made on any machine of any price. The only problem they have is that the machine sometimes takes a few seconds to find the vertical interval. To pay that kind of money, and get that high a quality of edit, anyone can surely wait the second it takes the machine to get itself together. No

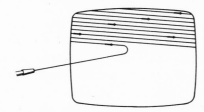

Assemble edit, scene B added to scene A.

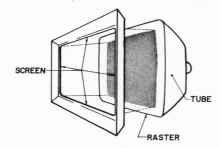

SCREEN

TUBE

RASTER

Insert edit, scene B inserted within scene A.

machine will edit exactly when the edit button is pressed; they all wait the fraction of a second that it might take for the vertical interval to get to the right spot. More expensive machines are able to lock onto it the first time around, the lower-priced ones get it a little later. This small detail is the only difference in the editing quality, however, and a mighty small price in perfection to pay, when the overall price of the machine is taken into account.

The other type of editing is called *insert* editing. This requires a more sophisticated editing deck, since the operation is more complex. Briefly, an insert edit is one in which you place information within an already existing tape. In other words, a scene begins, you drop in your material, and when the inserted material is over, you go smoothly back to the original information that was already on the tape. The electronic difference between assemble and insert editing is that in assemble editing, everything that was on the tape is erased as the new scene is added on. With insert editing, the control track from the segment being taped over is allowed to remain, and it supplies the sync during the edit. This makes the edits smoother, since the same control track runs for the entire length of the tape. You can use the insert-editing mode to do assemble editing, if you allow the entire tape to run through the machine in record. This will put down a control track that the vtr can follow when adding scenes.

Instead of just being able to add scene B onto scene A, and C onto B, etc., as in assemble editing, inserting information requires sophisticated techniques as well as equipment. Timing is critical, because if the edit lasts a little too long, the information below it on the tape will be lost. Your segments must be timed perfectly, so that you can come out of the insert right on time. Insert editing allows you to go back and put information onto a tape that was forgotten, or left out by mistake. You can also construct the production in such a way, so that you can add films, graphics, or interviews at a later date. During a production, a narrator can say, for example, "We will now watch an interview conducted with the head of ecological research for this county." If that interview was not informative enough, another one can be done of the same length, and inserted at that point.

Other than mechanical and electronic editing, there is a third method. You can *physically* edit the tape by cutting it. This is not

134

recommended, but it is the cheapest and quickest method of all. All you need is one vtr, an editing block, and some tape developer. Play the tapes on the vtr, and find the exact spots where you would like to make the edit. Place the end of the first scene next to the start on the second scene on the editing block. Dab some "Edivue" or similar developer on the edge of the tape, and the control track will appear as dots a half inch apart. Make your splice on these dots, and tape the edges of the two tapes together, putting the spots at the point of the splice. Use only special splicing tape that is made for video tape; no other tape is acceptable. This tape is extremely thin, and will not damage the tape or heads. Make sure you have applied the splicing tape to the back of the video tape and not on the side that faces the heads! If you have put the splicing tape on the oxide-covered part of the video tape, the side that has the recording on it, you run the risk of ruining the heads on your machine. This is a very expensive mistake, and one that there is no excuse for! Trim any exposed edges. When playing the tape back, the edit will appear as a wipe moving down across the screen. This is not too bad and, if your edits are neat, it is an interesting effect.

Physical editing offers you the chance to make on-the-scene edits at little expense. If your desire is to be as portable as possible, then this should be your main editing style. With experience, the edits get cleaner, and faster to make. However, with the low price of good editing decks today, it really pays to have one good deck for editing and dubbing.

We have explored the different ways of editing tapes: electronic, mechanical, and physical. We have also discussed the different kinds of edits that are available: the insert and assemble modes. There is no need to become involved in a discussion on specifically how to edit, since each machine comes with the directions for its particular needs, and any discussion would be obsolete as soon as this goes to press, inasmuch as electronic technology changes faster than we can keep up with it in print. Needless to say, editing will become easier and quicker as time goes on, and the equipment will become less and less expensive. By making up different patch cords for different machines, you should be able to use any combination of vtr's for your editing needs. All that is needed is some time to think, and a lot of creative imagination.

Audio is something of a problem in editing. Since the audio head is located physically after the video heads on vtr's, there is usually a slight delay before the audio of an edited segment will match the video. The video information is placed on the tape ahead of the audio, and this often results in a lag. Also, many machines create an audible click when an edit takes place that can be heard when the tape is played back. The only way to avoid the problem of the audio delay is to construct your taped information in such a way that there is no sound at all on the tape at the point of the edit. If at all possible, see if you can make the edit at a point where no one is talking, or where there is any repetitive sound, such as machine or traffic noise. If there is no sound present on the tape, no lag can possibly be heard. Where there is repetitive noise, it won't matter if the audio lags behind.

One way to solve the click problem is the same as the above: Try to make your edit at a point where there is no sound. Also, do not use an AGC control for the audio. On manual gain control, turn the gain all the way down. Right after you make the edit, quickly bring the gain up to the proper level. This will really work well only if there is no audio to disrupt. Otherwise, if you fade out the sound at the end of each segment, make your edit, then fade up again, any audio present will obviously be lost for a second or two. If the nature of the program allows this to happen, then you have no problem.

If the clicking sound really bothers you, you can edit the tape fully, and then go back and erase each click by using the audio dub mode on your machine at every edit point. This is a very long and tedious process, however, and should be attempted only after much thought about whether the tape really needs to be quite so perfect and, of course, if your vtr has an audio dub function.

The most successful method of avoiding audible edits is to add, or dub in, the sound after the video is fully edited. This requires a special kind of program, since you will never be able to lip sync people talking. You should dub audio only in a program that has a narrator's voice over the action, or one with a musical background. If you use *wild sound*, that is, sound that takes place during the scene you are taping, but not in sync, you can also dub after the video has been recorded. Don't try to lip sync the audio, you will only be wasting your time. Since sync sound is an inherent feature of television anyway, just accept the clicks or slight lag, and appreciate the medium for what it is.

136

Portable electrography is a new and different medium from broadcast television, and imperfect editing is one of the natures of the medium.

Once people accept it for that, and once technology provides all vtr's with good editors, editing will become just as routine as it is in film.

CHAPTER 16

SPECIAL EFFECTS

O nce you have made your first few tapes, you will begin to realize that there can be much more to portable video than aiming and shooting. This does not mean that the self-contained video system is not a medium all by itself; I think that we have established the fact that one Porta-Pak, by itself, is all one might ever need, to produce sophisticated and powerfully moving tapes. By giving up only a small amount of portability, and spending very little more, many new options will be open to you.

Some of the equipment involved, includes a *special effects generator,* a *Colorizer,* a *Gen-lock system,* a *switcher/fader,* and a number of additional monitors. None of this equipment costs over $1,000, and if you intend to get into serious dramatic, or even documentary, production, the outlay of cash will be rewarded many times over by the increase in sophistication. If your intention is to remain as flexible as possible, and be totally a community-oriented, street video type of operation, then I would still recommend a switcher/ fader, and possibly a Gen-lock device. Whether you are setting up in a truck, a storefront, a school, in industry, with cable, or independently, you should have all the flexibility you want in the field and still have good production back-up gear at your home base, for a minimum of cash outlay.

A simple *video switcher* is a small box with three, six, or twelve buttons on the front, and an equivalent number of inputs on the back. (Other amounts of inputs are available, but those are the most common.) With the right adaptors, a switcher will accept a Porta-Pak's camera signal. All the switcher does is to make clean, neat cuts between cameras. If you take two or three cameras with you, and patch them into the switcher, and then into the record deck, you can do all your editing on one master tape, with much neater results.

Remember that for every camera that feeds into your switcher, you will need a monitor to see what that camera is taking. For a three camera setup, you will need four monitors, one for each camera, and one, called the "line" monitor, to show what the composite, outgoing signal looks like. This multiple monitor setup is needed for all the special effects devices mentioned. You will need the extra monitors more for the other devices than for just a switcher, but it's a good idea to get used to using a "line" monitor.

A *switcher/fader* is the next most desirable piece of equipment, and also, the next most expensive. The inexpensive ones cost only a few hundred dollars. The *fader* part of the device allows you to switch from one camera to another, not by cutting as with the switcher, but by *dissolving*. When you dissolve from one camera to another, you gradually fade one camera's signal out, while fading another camera's signal in. You do this by moving a lever from one bank of a switcher's buttons, to another identical bank of buttons. When the fader lever is at the switcher "A" position, 100 percent of the video signal is passing through whatever button is depressed on row "A." As you move the lever toward the "B" bank of buttons, less of "A's" signal comes through, while more and more of "B's" signal comes out, until 100 percent of the video signal is coming from whatever camera's button is pushed down on row "B." The speed with which you move the lever, determines how fast the new picture comes onto the screen.

Moving the lever half way between the banks of buttons produces a *superimposition,* or *super.* A super can be used for an enormous amount of effects, but you must be careful how you use it. The nature of a super is similar to a double exposure in photography: 50 percent of each picture is seen on the screen at once. Since you are looking at two pictures simultaneously, you must be careful in your selection of the composition and information contained within the frames of each of the scenes you are using. Try not to use a picture that has an overabundance of picture detail. If the pictures you use are both too crowded, then you will lose whatever effect you were trying for; the composite picture will be much too detailed and crowded. If one scene is "busy" and the other not, then that is fine. If, however, both pictures on the cameras must be detailed, you will find that you can favor the more important of the two by moving the lever closer to the bank that controls the picture you want to make more visible, thereby giving that camera's video a higher percentage of the total picture. When you have a single object you want to super over any other picture, put that object in front of a plain background, black if possible. The simpler the background, the clearer the super.

The main use of supers is for titles. One camera picks up a title card that has white lettering on a black background. This is very often supered over live action, such as the opening shot of a program. Supers are also used to give information such as speakers' names, subtitles, process and part names in instructional programs, and instructions to follow concerning the visual portion of a program in training tapes.

Another type of super is known as the *decorative super*. You must be wary of overusing this type of effect, since it is pretty, and the temptation is great to use it too much. There is no place for decorative supers in a discussion-type program; cutting from camera to camera is fine for this type of show. With dramatic and musical tapes, however, slow, supering dissolves are the best way to carry through the smooth transitions called for. To keep a continuous flow of shots moving during a musical tape, for example, evenly spaced dissolves, timed to the mood of the piece, are very effective. Don't be tempted to hold a dissolve for too long as a super, however, since this almost always tends to ruin the flow of the segment, and to distract from what the audience should be paying attention to.

Entire programs can be built around a series of still pictures. If you allow the video to tell the story, and just use a minimum of narration, or none at all, with just a musical background, you will find this to be a very effective type of tape. Dissolve from still to still, with the speed of the dissolves determined by the mood and content of the piece. A description of this type of program is discussed in Chapter 8. We have done a number of these video-oriented programs and most have been quite beautiful. With the dissolve capacity, you can really open up very smooth, flowing possibilities that mellow the effect of the tape.

Switcher/faders are usually incorporated on *special effects generators (SEG)*, so if you can afford a switcher, try to go for the special effects generator as well. A simple special effects generator will offer you fades (a dissolve from a blank screen to a camera signal, or vice versa), cuts, dissolves between cameras, wipes (where it appears that one picture pushes another off the screen), and possibly a mat and a key control. The generator itself electronically mixes signals and delivers into the vtr sharp, clear composite pictures of your making.

Fading usually takes place at the beginning and end of a program, or between segments of that program. A blank screen is called "black." On a switcher, there is a button designated as "black." When that button is depressed, the recorder is fed a signal equal to a camera's signal, but it is blank. When opening a show, the best way to draw the viewer in, is to fade in from black. At first the viewer gets involved with the blank screen (it really happens), and then, as you fade in from black and the first scene begins to appear on the screen, he is in sync with you. As McLuhan points out, books, or print in general, "contains" information for the reader, while television "involves" the viewer (Introduction to *Understanding Media*). People become immersed in experiencing video; they virtually get drawn into the happenings on the screen. NBC discovered

Switcher/fader with special effects generator. Courtesy Grass Valley Group, Inc.

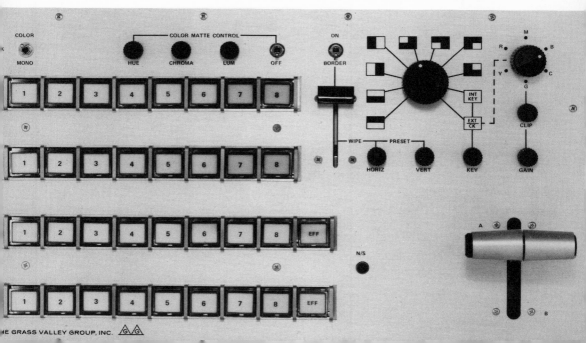

long ago that when running a movie, it is best not to start with the credits, or even an introduction to the station's title card, but to just start the movie, and super the title and credits over the film, once it has started. They do this, because they have discovered that once a viewer has begun watching a film on television, no matter how bad it may be, he is disinclined to get up and change the station, or especially, turn off the set. The path of least resistance is to continue watching the film. If the credits and title were shown first, and then they went to a commercial, there would be time and motivation to make a change. Beware of this technique, but accept it as a lesson of how well the networks do understand some very important aspects of the medium.

You can also learn much about certain powerful effects that TV has on people, since the networks must do studies about this, as they pertain to consumerism. When you begin to realize the tremendous research that goes into getting people interested in the beginning of a show, so that they will watch the remainder of the program after the first commercial, you can see that it goes well beyond the opening fade-in of the program. However, for our purposes, fading-in to the start of a program serves us fine. Use it because it works.

Fading, or dissolving, to black, is called *fading-out*. Fading-in to a picture from black, conversely, is known as *fading-in*. To separate different and varying program segments from one another, a short fade in and out of black is very good. People are accustomed to the use of fades. Most are unaware of this, but subconsciously they expect certain things to happen when a fade occurs, so you can use this conditioning to your advantage.

Many cameras and/or special effects generators have a switch that will reverse the polarity of the camera's signal, creating a negative image. This can be a very strange and unique effect that looks quite eerily beautiful, if properly used. Reversing the polarity of a politician while giving a speech can be quite poignant and subtle, if he is that type of man. Strange landscapes can be created, and if you super a positive person over a negative landscape, you can get some rather interesting results. The amount of uses for this type, and for any kind of special effect, are limited only by your imagination. I must caution you once again, however: A tape with no special effects at all, is much better than one with too many, or

142

poorly used, ones. Some other uses of negative video are explosions —a quick flip to reverse polarity and back is a very effective atom bomb technique. This can also be accomplished by adjusting the beam control of your camera, if there is one. (It is automatic in the Rover camera, for example.) But if you have access to the beam, turning it up past its desired setting will produce extreme brightness, and then it will flip the picture into negative. When properly done, this is quite realistic. If you don't have any explosions to portray, or politicians, or landscapes, you'll come up with something, since this one is too good to forgo.

As simply as the camera can handle polarity reversal, it can also do what is known as *sweep reversal*. Horizontal sweep reversal will produce a mirror image, where right and left are reversed. Vertical sweep reversal will flip the picture upside down. Vertical reversal has been used mainly for humor, but again, its uses are up to you. A simultaneous reversal of both horizontal and vertical sweeps can be accomplished easily, and that produces some startling reactions in the viewers. The sweep reversal is accomplished in the camera or in the camera control unit. Sometimes there is an available switch, often there is not, so check your camera's specs.

Wipes are used fairly often. They are more often used partially wiped as inserts, than as a way of going from one picture to another. A *horizontal wipe* inserts a picture on the left- or right-hand side of the screen (you decide where to start it), and it pushes the existing

Vertical wipe.

picture off the screen, as it moves across. The *vertical wipe* does the same thing, much the way a theater curtain opens up on, or closes down on, the scene on a stage. A horizontal wipe left halfway across the screen is known as a *split screen*. When using split screens, you must be careful to properly frame your cameras. If Camera 1 is to be on the left-hand side of the split screen, and Camera 2 on the right, the information to be shown on Camera 1 must be framed to the right-hand side of that camera's field of view, as the left side of its field of view will not be shown. The opposite is true for Camera 2; the information here must be framed on the left side. Even if the right side is totally blank, it doesn't matter, since it won't be shown.

A very good use for a split screen is to help the viewer maintain his orientation. If you are showing a potter doing some very intricate work on a wheel, start with a medium shot of both the potter and the wheel. Then go to a split screen that shows the potter in the medium shot (MS) on the left, while a close-up is shown on the right, of his fingers working the clay. You can then go to the close-up alone. The split screen shows the viewer precisely where the potter is in relation to his hands and the wheel. It is amazing how many people can get quickly disoriented when you go to a close-up like this. If they can watch both the medium shot and the close-up for a few seconds, it helps them place a perspective on what they are seeing.

You can also have a person on screen seemingly push one scene away while his scene comes on. You can do this either vertically or horizontally. If you should ever need an effect like that, keep in mind that the staging of this particular effect involves careful timing and framing.

When you get into the more expensive special effects generators, you will find that wipes come in a great variety of shapes; I've seen as many as 26 on one mixer. They look like diamonds, little squares, triangles, teeth, squiggly lines, circles, etc. Some mixers have a device known as a "joy stick." The joy stick allows you to move certain effects to any part of the screen; it's usually hooked up with the circle. By manipulating the joy stick, which is a lever that can be moved in any direction, you can place the circle in a corresponding spot of the picture screen. The circle contains whatever you punch up on the mixer, and is used most often to insert faces. I don't advise laying out the considerable amount of money these types of effects would entail, because even in commercial broadcasting, you very rarely ever

144

Corner insert.

Horizontal wipe.

Vertical wipe.

see these used. If the networks don't use something for which they've paid a lot of money, you can be assured that it just doesn't work the way it should. If you absolutely need to insert someone's grinning face into a tree trunk, let us say, then you can almost always rent the effects generator for the time that you need it. I highly recommend that you look into renting equipment instead of purchase, since you will probably come out way ahead, and not be stockpiling devices that contain rarely used effects. In most cities you can rent studios and/or individual equipment by the hour. The expense of renting the gear might discourage you from doing the fancy special effect you are trying for, and in the long run, your production might be better off without it.

A *mat* electronically inserts, or cuts, one picture into another. The mat is a selective effect that will only insert a high contrast subject onto another picture. It is used most often for titles. The mat is similar to a super, but differs in that you can see through a super into the picture underneath. (A super is 50 percent of each picture.) You cannot see through a mat. The matted title is solid white or black, and any picture under it is removed by the generator. It is cleaner and sharper than a super, and therefore, much more pleasing to use, if you have the capacity.

An interesting use of the mat, is to brightly light a singer's face, for example, and mat it over another view of the singer. By controlling the sensitivity of the mat, which is an inherent feature of a mat, you can create very interesting visual images. Place the matted view of the singer off to a side of the screen, so that you can see the singer both normally and ghostly matted.

The *video key* is similar to the mat in that it electronically inserts another image onto a picture already on the screen. It differs, however, in that instead of having a high contrast image of the object that you are portraying, you can actually see the object as it really is. Where the singer's face appears all white or all black in a mat, it looks just like the singer in a key. You also need three cameras to make it work most effectively. Using two cameras, you can insert the action on one camera over a background supplied by another camera. If you need a location for a background that you just can't get to, use a still photograph of the location and key your action over the still photograph. It may not look exactly like the real thing, but it comes close, and works well enough to get your point across.

146

If you can use three cameras, you can get some very interesting effects. The three-camera key gets you into some real video experiences. One camera supplies the background. The second camera picks up any shape you may put in front of it. As in matting, when you are using something to mat, or "key off" of, it should ideally be white on black. The white should be the title in the mat, and the shape of your cutout for a key.

Let's use a heart shape, in a tape of a friend's wedding, for example. You would cut out a heart-shaped piece of white paper, and attach it to a black piece of paper. The third camera picks up the scene for the insert. In the tape of our friend's wedding, we can duplicate the photograph that appears in nearly everyone's wedding picture album. The first camera shows a tree trunk, the second has the shot of the heart, and the third has a close-up of the happy couple. In the composite image shown on the line monitor, we see a heart-shaped insert of the couple, placed over the trunk of the tree. Romantic? That's questionable, but you can see how shapes can be used to insert information in the mood of the program.

The best and most pure video effect there is, works only with color equipment, but it warrants some discussion here. *Chroma-keying* works on the mat and key principle, but is more sophisticated. Instead of using black for the background of the material to be keyed, they use blue. Everything that is blue will disappear, and whatever is being picked up on a second camera will be shown as the background. Chroma-key matting is used extensively on news shows. The viewer sees the newsman sitting in front of what seems to be a window on the scene of a disaster, for example. His desk looks as if it were out in the street of a tornado-ravaged town. What he is actually sitting in front of is a large blue screen, and what is actually taking place is that the chroma-key device is inserting a film or tape of the scene onto all that is blue on the first camera, or all the background around the newsman. Of course, if he were to wear a blue sport jacket, his chest and arms would disappear, into the background. Some announcers must wear brown contact lenses over their bright blue eyes, when close-ups are taken, or their eyes would appear as holes in the announcer's head. Chroma-key is sharp, clear, and easy to use. When color gear gets down to a reasonable price range, which won't be long, it will be a valuable tool to have.

Cuts, fades, dissolves, supers, wipes, matting, and keying are about all you can expect to get out of a $600 special effects generator. That is plenty to work with, and if you can buy the generator, it's worth the investment.

At this point in time, it is not within the state of the art to mix two taped half-inch signals through a special effects generator. You can, however, mix a taped and live signal by using a *Gen-lock* system. The Gen-lock device takes the sync from the tape machine and drives the camera with that. This allows you to put titles on pre-recorded tapes, for example. A cheaper way of mixing taped signals is to optically mix two recorded tapes by playing them back through good monitors, and aim a camera at each monitor. Then feed this signal through your special effects generator. It won't look perfect, but it's not too bad. Simple Gen-lock systems start at about $400.

While good color half-inch vtr's can be obtained for around $1,000, there is not yet a camera to feed them a color signal for anything around that price. You can use a device known as a *Colorizer*, to add color information to a black-and-white tape. Keeping in mind that you don't need special tape to record electronic color information (this astounds photographers), you can play a tape through a Colorizer and produce some fascinating results. At times the colors produced are almost lifelike, which is amazing, since the device puts

Simple, one-camera video feedback.

out totally random information. More often, however, the results are wild and fantastic. You can use the Colorizer either on live cameras or off taped signals. You can also change the color controls as the device is operating, so as to have even more control over what is happening, but don't expect to use this device to add natural color to your black-and-white gear. Colorizers are going for under $1,000 now, and will cost less, I'm sure, as technology catches up to what we want.

An effect that you would have to call "special" is what you get when you begin to deal with *video feedback*. Simply explained, video feedback is the same thing you get when holding a microphone in front of a speaker that is playing back what the mike is picking up; you hear a loud, high-pitched whistle. That is a sound being repeated over and over again, to the exclusion of all other sounds. Video feedback is the same, except that you are repeating a visual signal.

The most simple form of video feedback is to point a camera at its own monitor. Zoom in on the screen so that all that is filling the viewfinder is the inside of the monitor screen, no edges. You will see patterns begin to appear, usually taking the shape of light grey, or white, amorphous shapes, moving about the screen. These shapes will tend to pulse in a random sequence. By moving the camera slightly you will find that you can control the shape and speed of these blobs. A good deal of experimenting is called for, and with practice, you will be able to repeat certain effects that you like. Add appropriate music, and you've got a pure video piece.

The most exciting thing about video feedback is that it is pure television. There are no people, objects, lights, or any other artificial intrusion. All the images seen on the screen are made strictly by the equipment itself. Video feedback is a pure video art form, and, I believe, an entirely different medium than portable video, and especially, than broadcast television. It must be considered a new medium since it is so totally created by itself. Color *video synthesizers* can also be considered in this classification. Synthesizers were developed by video-artist-engineers such as Chin Lui, Eric Siegal, and Nam June Paik. They are much the same as an audio synthesizer, although not yet as elaborate as the Moog (just a matter of time). The devices create their own video signal internally without a camera. They can be played like a piano, so you can sit down at a keyboard-like console, and compose a video piece while watching your effects on a screen.

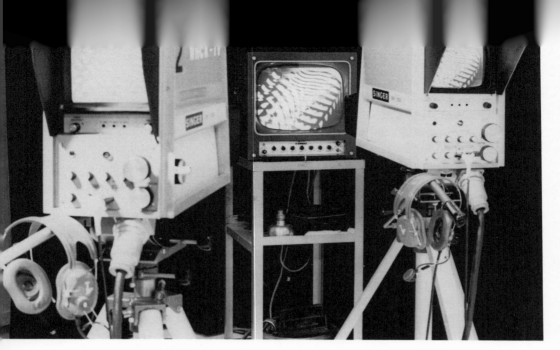

Two-camera video feedback.

More elaborate video feedback effects can be achieved with two cameras and a special effects genrator. Aim both cameras at a line monitor and feed them through either the mat or key portions of the generator. By moving the cameras slightly, and by changing the mat shading and key sensitivity, hauntingly beautiful effects can be achieved. Endless black-and-white rippling triangles that seem to go back into infinity, white globes and waving black lines oozing and darting about, are some of the inherent effects that you will see. If you want to move away from pure video a little, you can add extraneous objects such as people or clocks or anything else that will move.

A classic feedback use is to have a dancer perform in front of one camera. Have the other camera aimed at a line monitor. Mat the dancer's image over the camera that is aimed at the monitor. By moving the second camera slightly around the monitor screen, you will see a totally white image of the dancer, getting smaller and smaller as the image retreats back into infinity. By imparting a slight motion to the camera, you will make the tail end of the receding series of images seemingly whip around. This action is similar to ice skaters who form a "snake." While the skater on the inside of the line barely moves at all, like our second camera, the tail end of the

150

line whips about at high speed, like the rear image on the monitor's screen. This effect can be done without matting the signal of the dancer, and it is like sitting in a barber's chair in one of those barber shops that has mirrors along both the front and rear walls. When looking into the mirror in front of you, your image can be seen on the mirror on the rear wall, reflected on the front mirror, and so on, until your reflected image becomes too small to be seen.

Video feedback is an interesting effect, both with and without the special effects generator, and with one or two cameras; try it, you'll be glad you found out about feedback.

A short section of this chapter will be devoted to nonelectronic special effects, so I will call this brief section:

Optical Special Effects

The most widely used optical effect is *rear projection,* which is known as *RP*. Broadcast rear projection involves very expensive screens which are specially treated, and highly sophisticated projectors, which are also quite expensive. There is no need for you to get involved with that kind of expense. You can use plastic material that is used for shower curtains. It comes in sheets of up to 100 feet, and is relatively inexpensive. It can be purchased from building supply houses, lumber yards, or good hardware stores. They may not have it in stock, so plan ahead. Ask for translucent white plastic, two to three mills thick. When you get the plastic, cut it to the size you need, and then reinforce the edges with weatherstripping tape. Get the two-inch–width tape; it's remarkably strong, and will take great stress. Put the tape along the outside edges of your cutout section. Make a frame out of 2″ x 4″ boards (1″ x 2″ may work if you are going to make a small RP screen). Staple the plastic, smoothly, to the frame. Stapling may horrify some broadcast types, but if you're careful, it works fine; just make sure you have the plastic even and tight all around.

Now that you have an official RP screen, some discussion of how you can use it is called for. The most obvious use is to project a background onto the screen as has been mentioned previously. If you can't get yourself and your Rover to a particular location, use a slide of that scene (assuming, of course, that getting the slide is easier than getting the actual location) and project it onto the back of the RP screen. Any people appearing in the production can then be shown in front of the screen. This works remarkably well, and although I don't recommend that you try to fool someone with this technique, and tell them that you were actually there, it is quite life-like. One thing to remember is that when using an RP setup, instead of loading slides upside down and backward, the way you would in front projection, you must put them in only upside down, since they will be seen through the screen, not reflected off it.

Another interesting use of an RP screen involves placing all the action behind the screen, so that all the action appears visually as silhouettes. A handy device to have when doing this kind of program is an overhead projector. Very detailed scenery can be designed on 8" x 10" transparencies and projected onto the screen. You can use the overhead projector to throw all the light needed for the silhouettes and the projected scenery. If an overhead is not available to you, any strong directional light will do, even a slide projector. Do not use a movie projector, however, since the shutter blades will create rolling lines on the screen which are discernible only when watching the action on a monitor. Super 8 films will project well, for some reason, but not 16mm, because it has an effective speed of one-fiftieth of a second. Television operates at one-sixtieth of a second, which causes sync problems, and you get that rolling bar going through your picture.

When setting up a program of this type, decide just what kind of scenery you will want to use. Simple cardboard cutouts work well, as will anything that will give you a good shadow image on the screen. Drawing the scenery on transparencies is the easiest and cheapest way to do it. You will have to experiment with size a little at first, but once you get it down, you will see just how far back to place the projector, and where to put the people between the projector and the screen.

This technique is very effective when you are working with people who are not sure that they want to appear on television. Once they realize that only their shadow will be seen and only their voices heard, they will probably be much more willing to participate in your production. After these people see how easy and painless the whole thing was, it is unlikely that you will be able to keep them from

152

using the medium to express themselves from then on. This shadow technique can also be used when taping someone who legitimately can't be seen: undercover agents discussing their work, for example.

Another simple optical special effect is to play around with the front portion of the lens. Not the lens itself, of course, but with material placed just ahead of the lens. The most often used technique of this type is the dreamy effect of having the edges of a scene out of focus, while the center is sharp. This is used a good deal in broadcasting for singers doing love songs. Take a large-sized Dixie cup and cut out the bottom. Tape some clear acetate over this hole, and smear Vaseline around the edges of the acetate. Now put the open large end of the cup over the front of the lens, and slide the whole thing over your lens. How simple and cheap can an effect be? Any number of things can be done with this paper cup device. A good idea is to paint the inside of the cup black, so as to make it more inconspicuous.

You will discover uses for this device as well as for all the others I have mentioned in this chapter, either as I have described them, or hopefully, in ways that no one has even considered yet. Don't be conventional when it comes to special effects. Mould existing effects to your needs. Improvise, and above all, invent! The only limit, once again, is your imagination. Some of the most ingenious effects I've ever seen have been done by people who are only moderately familiar with the equipment. If you have an idea for a particular way of presenting some information that won't get in the way of the presentation of that information, try it out—the medium really is the message, so use the medium to its fullest capacity to help fortify your message's meaning.

CHAPTER 17

GRAPHICS

Graphics are an essential element in television production. In television, the term *graphics* applies to all two-dimensional visual materials used on camera. Maps, title cards, illustrations, photographs, and graphs are all considered to be graphics. Graphics are used mainly for titling and identification, for visual representations of something being discussed on camera for clarity, for purely visual effects, and to help set up electronic special effects.

Three factors should be considered in the design of any graphic material: the first is the *gray scale* response; next is the *style* of the graphics; and the last is the *size* and *clarity* of the material being presented.

Black-and-white television registers all colors as different shades of gray. A ten-step gray scale has been developed, but it takes exceptional equipment to represent ten shades of gray on most television equipment. A seven-step scale is more common. As we know from the first chapter, pure whites and blacks cannot be produced on television, thereby eliminating two steps of a ten-step gray scale. On a seven-step scale, the first step is off-white, or "television white." The seventh step is very dark gray, or "television black."

When dealing with color, we see three things as being important: *hue*, or the color itself (red, blue, yellow); *brightness*, or how light or dark a color is; and *saturation*, or *chroma*, which refers to the strength of the color (pale yellow or deep purple). Black-and-white television is, by definition, insensitive to hue (color) and chroma (shade). The only thing that registers is the brightness of an object. Colors that are not at all alike to the eye, may have the same brightness or reflective quality, and come out as the same step of a gray scale. For example, red and some shades of green would look exactly alike on monochrome television. For this reason, you must be very careful when working with color graphics. Even if you are doing the original taping in color, it is very likely that somewhere along the line your program will be seen on a black-and-white receiver. As a general rule, don't use pastel colors for graphics, since they will just appear to be similar shades of gray on the screen. When using colorful graphics, always check them on a black-and-white monitor before committing them to tape.

The next important thing to consider when preparing graphic material is the *style* of the graphic itself. Simply stated, make sure that the graphic you use fits the theme of your show. A humorously lettered title card for a serious program will not put the viewer into the proper frame of mind for your presentation. If you have laboriously prepared a tape, don't ruin it by using a hastily hand-lettered title card for an introduction. Take some time in preparing them; sloppy or inappropriate graphics can do much to ruin the effect of a program.

The last category may be the most important. The *size* and the *clarity* of the material on the graphic have some limitations imposed on them by the nature of the television medium. If you don't allow for these limitations, your material will look sloppy and amateurish.

The television screen allows only a limited amount of information to be presented at one time. The small screen size, coupled with the fact that most people sit many feet away from the set, means that you must prepare graphics with large, clearly identifiable letters, drawings, and objects. You cannot make the graphic appear too "busy." Uncluttered, simple materials will always look better than elaborate, detailed representations.

The single most important thing to keep in mind when preparing graphics is the *aspect ratio* of the television screen. Television operates with an aspect ratio of 3:4. That is, the screen of every set is three units high, and four units wide. All picture information, to be best shown, must conform to this 3:4 aspect ratio.

155

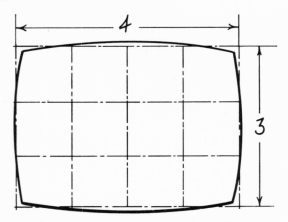

The 3:4 aspect ratio of a television picture.

When preparing a title card, for example, you must consider not only the aspect ratio, but also the amount of picture loss that occurs between the camera and the receiver. What you see on the camera or vtr monitor is rarely what will be seen on the average receiver. Monitors are *underscanned*, and receivers are *overscanned*. An overscanned picture is one where the extreme edges of the picture fall on the raster, outside the area we see as the screen. In this way, the information around the edges of any television picture is lost to the viewer watching on anything but a monitor that is underscanned. An underscanned monitor is one that not only shows all the picture information, but even has a space between the edge of the picture and the border of the screen.

Since virtually all receivers are overscanned, as are some monitors, you must allow for this in your graphics, by allowing for a border around the edges of the card, and by keeping all the information on the card right in the center.

The material easiest to use for graphics is an 11" x 14" sheet of stiff board. These can be purchased inexpensively in any art supply store, and sometimes they are even called "TV Cards." To save money, you can buy large sheets of poster board and cut them to size yourself. If you use an 11" x 14" card, keep all your material within a 9" x 12" area in the middle of the board. This will give you the proper aspect ratio, and a good border as well. When the cameraman is setting up the shot, he should frame the entire 11" x 14" board as best he can, with the edges of the board reaching the edges of his

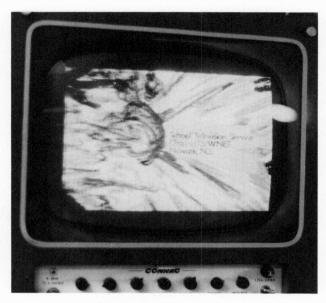

Underscanned picture on video monitor.

viewfinder screen. When played back, the information contained within the 9″ x 12″ area should fit perfectly in the center of the receiver's screen.

Try not to ever use more than ten words on one card. Working within a 9″ x 12″ area should limit this since, in order to fit in more words, the lettering would have to be very small and virtually un-readable on the screen. Before you start to letter the board, make light pencil marks on it outlining the 9″ x 12″ area. When lettering, use bold letters, as thin ones might be smaller than the resolving power of the receiver and, consequently, they will be invisible on that receiver. For the same reason, space the letters far enough apart so that they will be separated clearly on the screen. Lastly, make sure you align them carefully. It is hard enough to line up graphics on camera so that they look straight. If they are crooked to start with, your picture will really look terrible.

Unless you are an expert letterer and illustrator, or unless it really doesn't matter, don't hand-letter your title cards. "Transfer Type," "Letter On," and the other press-on letters are the best way to letter anything. These letters come on sheets with an ample supply of all letters. All you have to do is to place the plastic sheet over the

157

Reynolds Tapesign Leteron.

card, line up the letter you want to use, and rub it with any hard object, such as a dull pencil point. The letter is removed from the sheet and fixed onto your graphic. These letters come in all sizes, styles, and colors. If you intend to super white letters onto a scene, use white type on a black card. If you are going to super black letters on a light scene, use black type on a light blue card. Use a light blue card instead of a white one, since white reflects much too much light, and the resulting super will appear washed out.

Another slightly more sophisticated lettering process is the "Reynolds Printa Sign." I have attempted to avoid using brand names in this book, except where the product is clearly worth using. In this case the Printa Sign system is well worth its cost, which is around $150. This method takes a little longer than the instant press-on letters, but it produces larger and clearer lettering than just about anything short of professional and costly lettering machines. You take various type fonts that are available with the

158

machine, and by a simple and relatively quick engraving system, the letters are transferred to a white (or black) tape that has a clear adhesive coating. By picking up the clear coating, you can place the letters on your graphic card and align them perfectly, since they can be positioned without attaching them to the card. Once you have the line of lettering exactly where you want it, you press them down onto the card with a roller, or "brayer," and peel back the clear sheet. Your letters are in place, properly spaced and aligned.

Photographs can be mounted on cards, either with a dry mounting press (if you have access to one) or with contact cement. Lettering can be applied on the surface of the photograph or, if you don't wish to mar it, on a clear piece of acetate placed above the picture.

All sorts of things can and should be used as graphics. Interesting openings can be done by printing a title neatly on a girl's stomach. When she moves out of frame, the scene behind her can be focused in to start the production. Another idea is to use a window for the printing, when the title has been on long enough, open the window and focus on the events in the room inside.

A good rule of thumb for the length of time any printed material should remain on the screen is three times as long as it takes you to read it. By reading the card slowly three times you can allow for the various reading abilities of the viewers.

Slides and overhead transparencies make good graphics, and have been used with a great amount of success. The only drawback to slides is that if you don't have a film chain, you must shoot them with a television camera in a darkened room. This may be an inconvenience but a worthwhile one if the slides are of particular importance. Overhead transparencies are very good, because you don't have to darken the room, and they provide a large area over which the camera can pan and zoom if needed. Also, overheads provide an option called *overlays*. Overlays are clear plastic sheets of acetate, as are the transparencies themselves, which can be placed over another sheet already on the projector. In this way, additional information can be added, as much and as fast as you desire.

Graphics are an essential part of any television production. Good ones can only help to make the electrographer's point clearer, and to provide even more information to the viewer. Hopefully, this chapter provided you with the basic information you need to prepare informative, clear, and valuable graphic material.

CHAPTER 18

DUPLICATING VIDEO TAPES

After laboring over his productions, the electrographer usually has a desire to show these tapes to more people than are in his television production class, and to people other than his friends and associates. Many tapes of exceptional beauty and vastly informative content are never seen by more than a small handful of people. This is a crime, and something should be done about it. It is very frustrating indeed to know that you have a great tape, and no way to have it shown.

It is virtually impossible for a person working with helical scan equipment to have his tapes broadcast over the air. The FCC, in an access-limiting move, has set standards for broadcast signals well above what all but the newest and most expensive one-inch recorders can produce. This makes it hard to show your tapes to large groups of people simultaneously. The other alternative is cable television. There are no restrictions, as yet, on the signal quality transmitted over cable. Your only problem is getting the company to play your tape over their system, and then advertising the fact that it will be shown. This, we leave up to your own ingenuity.

The only other way to get your tapes shown, for now, at any rate, is to hold showings in your town or city, or to make duplicates, *dubs,* that can be sent to other electrographers and video people in other areas, for them to show. Whether you show them yourself, or

160

if others do (including cable companies), you will need to make copies of your work.

If the fact that your tapes can be easily copied bothers you, then you are working in the wrong medium. Video tape is one of the easiest of all mediums to duplicate. If you can show a tape, then you can most likely make a copy. Copyright laws serve the useful purpose of making sure that the creator of a work gets credit for it, and, in most cases, gets paid, for his efforts. However, copyrighting has also served to withhold information, and since the Media Revolution is also the information access revolution, you must accept the fact that if your tapes are good, they will be copied.

Hopefully, you will receive recognition for the original material, and the royalty that may be due. But if you don't, there is nothing you can do short of stopping your production of tapes. The Xerox machine has done quite a job on the print copyright laws, and the outcome of that battle has not yet been resolved. If you plan on making a copy of someone else's tape, or using segments of it in your production, get in touch with him, if possible, and work out some kind of agreement. If you can't find the creator of a tape you plan on copying or using, give him clear credit for the information you received from him. It is always possible he will see the tape and then get in touch with you to work things out. We must work closely together on this, since it is a problem that will get worse, as more and more tapes are made.

There are a number of ways to duplicate tapes. The first is the easiest and cheapest, although it is also the most time-consuming. Put the master tape on one machine, and feed it directly into another vtr. This will give you one *second-generation* tape. To make two tapes, you have to rewind both machines, put a new tape on the second machine, and repeat the process.

The next method allows you to make up to three tapes at once. It is called *looping*. In dubbing, the machine that has the master tape on it is called, unsurprisingly, the *master machine*. The vtr's that record the information fed from the master machine are romantically known as *slave machines*. You can feed the signal from the master machine into the first slave machine. If you then attach cables to the video and audio-out jacks on the slave machine, you can feed another slave vtr. This will usually work well enough on two machines. It the signal is exceptionally strong, you will be able to feed a third machine with this unamplified signal. Before you attempt using three slave vtr's, make a test tape to see what your results will be.

A better way to feed slave machines, and a method that will allow you an unlimited number of dubs (the limit is only the number of machines that are available to you), is to use *video distribution amplifiers,* or *VDA*'s. A standard VDA will split one video signal four ways, and boost the strength of each of the four to the perfect one-volt signal. VDA's that will give you more than four outputs are available, but it is recommended that you get two VDA's with four outputs, instead of one with many outputs. By having more than one VDA, you can split more than one signal at once, if the need should ever arise.

To make four tapes, feed the master signal into the VDA, and feed four machines from its outputs. If more dubs are required, feed three vtr's from the VDA, and feed the fourth video-out signal into another VDA. You can keep doing the same thing for as many machines as you have available to serve as slaves. Theoretically, every dub with this amplified system should be every bit as good as a second-generation tape can be. The use of a proc amp between the master vtr and the first VDA will help to insure this.

The last method of duplicating tapes is to do it electronically. This is expensive because the equipment is expensive, but in the not distant future, maybe by the time you read this book, time rentals will be available for duplicating on these machines. The greatest advantage of electronic duplication is that each dub is as perfect as the original. There are no such things as second-generation tapes —all tapes are identical. The other advantage is that they operate at very high speeds. When using master and slave vtr's, you can only dub in real time. If you have an hour tape, it will take an hour to copy it. On an electronic duplicating machine, this is not the case, since the tape is not copied in the same manner as in the vtr-to-vtr method.

Panasonic has the best system that really works. Other systems have problems because air very often gets in between the master tape and the copy. Since this is a contact method of duplication, the air bubbles will cause some of the information to be lost on the copy. Panasonic's system, called the "Video Tape Printer," or "VTP," uses what they call a "Bilifar Tape Winding System," which evidently

162

has solved the problem of air bubbles, and tape slippage, which was another problem that could arise.

The process is relatively simple. The master tape is threaded onto a machine that also has a slave tape threaded on it. These two tapes are passed under a pressure roller, and wound up into one big reel of tape, which is made up of one layer of the master tape, followed by one layer of the slave tape, etc., throughout the entire reel. Then, a magnetic field is passed through the whole reel, and a mirror image of the master tape is created on the slave tape. Both tapes are then rewound, and removed from the machine. Next, the master tape is put aside, and the mirror image tape is put onto another machine, similar to the first. A blank tape is also put on this machine, and the process is repeated. This time the mirror-image tape produces images on the blank tape that are correct. When these tapes are rewound, and the new tape removed, it is an exact copy of the master tape. The process may seem complicated, but it takes only two minutes to produce each tape. To get the first tape it takes four minutes, because the mirror-image tape must be produced, but each successive tape takes only two minutes.

The incredible speed at which the tapes are duplicated, and the perfection of the results, are really awe-inspiring. With the possibility of producing tapes at such a high speed, mass duplication and distribution of video tapes can become a reality. With a system like this available, the responsibility lies with the electrographer to produce the programming that will keep the VTP's busy.

SCRIPTING

A script is a print readout of all the video and audio portions of a television program. There are three basic kinds of scripts: the *full script*, the *semiscript*, and the *shot sheet*.

The *full script* contains every spoken word, all the video instructions, all the stage directions, and all the miscellaneous information that may be needed, such as additional sound effects, etc. The fully scripted show is usually a dramatic presentation, since very few other kinds of programs need this much attention to detail. You really need to fully script a show only if you must know every bit of action in precise detail.

When preparing your script, divide your page in half lengthwise. Use the left-hand portion of the page for the video instructions, and the right-hand side for the audio. All the audio directions should be typed in CAPITAL letters. All spoken words should be in upper- and lowercase letters, as you would normally expect. This will eliminate any confusion between directions and dialogue. Otherwise, you might hear an actor say, "Goodnight, my darling, exit camera left."

Video directions can be typed normally, in upper- and lowercase letters, since there should be no danger of anyone attempting to read them aloud. Also, they will be easier for you to read. Certain abbreviations are used in video directions, the most common ones are simple. CU means close-up. MS is a medium shot. LS is long shot. XCU or XLS means an extreme close-up or long shot. Medium-two-shot is shortened to M2S. Most people use their own type of short-hand, and you can use whatever is most understandable to you.

This is an example of a full script:

VIDEO	AUDIO
—Fade into MS of Host	BACKGROUND MUSIC UP
—Slow zoom in to CU	FADE OUT MUSIC
—CU Host	*HOST:* Good evening. Welcome
—Cut to title card	to "The Drama Hour."
"The Emerald"	Tonight's
—Cut to LS host, pan left as	performance is "The Emerald,"
Host walks off screen to	by Barbara Hoctor.
camera right.	FADE IN THEME
—Fade to black	THREE LOUD KNOCKS ON
—Fade in to LS of stage	DOOR
—Zoom in on door	*HARRY,* FROM BEHIND
—Door opens, Harry enters.	DOOR:
—Cut to MS Harry	Anybody home?
	Hello, I'm here. . . .

ETC.

In stage directions, "camera right" refers to the right side of the screen, or the right side of the stage as you look at it from the audience. This may be confusing to actors who work in legitimate theater, as "camera-right" means "stage-left" to them. Always imagine the stage as if you were looking at it through a camera viewfinder.

A *semiscripted* format is used in a program where certain portions of the dialogue are known in advance, as are some of the camera directions. An interview show is a good example of a situation that calls for a semiscript.

The following is an example of a semiscript:

VIDEO	AUDIO
—Fade in to host	HOST: Hello, our guest today
—Cut to MS Hoch	is the basketball star, Bob Hoch.
—Cut to LS of both	Tell me, Bob, . . .
—Cut to M2S	INTERVIEW CONTINUES AD
—SHOTS AS NEEDED	LIB
—MS Host	HOST:
—Fade to black	Thank you, Bob.

Making the Media Revolution

The last kind of script, and probably the one most used in portable video applications, is the *shot sheet*. The shot sheet is used to list the shots needed, in the order in which they will ultimately be edited together. No audio is included, since this will most likely be dubbed in after the tape is edited.

A shot sheet would look like this:

1. LS river
2. Slow pan until sewage plant is in center on screen
3. Zoom in on waste pouring from pipes.
4. CU pipes
   ETC.

There are no absolute rules on scripting. These three examples have been included so that you could have some guidelines in determining what type of scripting you will use.

HOW TO MAKE STANDARD AUDIO AND VIDEO CONNECTORS

In this section, the elements of soldering the various connectors that you will need are shown visually. The *UHF* connector shown is used for coaxial cable, which generally carries the video and/or sync signal. The *Cannon* connector is used for low impedance audio sources. The *phone* plug is for high impedance audio sources. All plugs shown are male connectors, the females; or *jacks,* are connected to their cables in the same manner. *Mini* plugs and *phono* plugs are attached to cables in the same manner as the phone plug.

A vise is always recommended to hold the connector while soldering, as it gives you a solid steady support while your hands are holding the solder and soldering gun.

Tinning is the process of melting a small amount of hot solder on the tips of the wires and pins before joining them together.

The following photographs outline the steps involved in making up all the cables you will need in electrography:

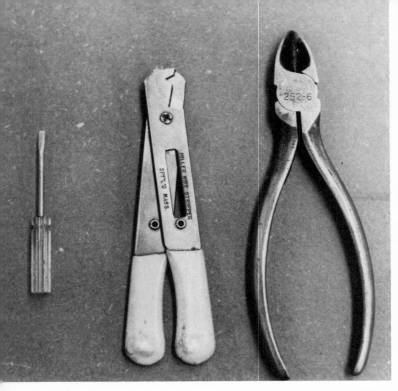

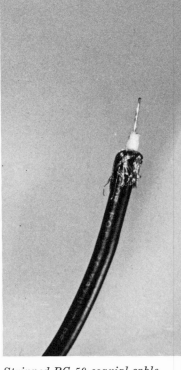

Tools needed for making connectors: miniature screwdriver,
wire stripper, and diagonal cutter.

Stripped RG-59 coaxial cable
with shielding folded back.

Make sure shell is on
cable before soldering.

Soldering the tip.

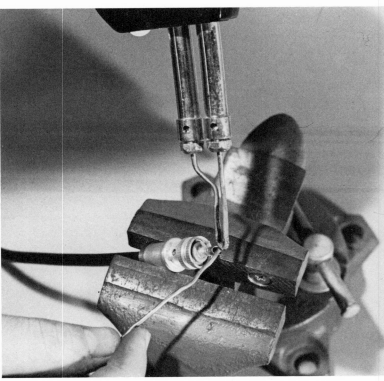

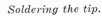

Disassembled male
Cannon connector.

Completed UHF plug—note that
solder on tip should be shiny.

Stripped two-conductor
shielded cable.

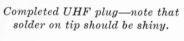

Make sure shell is on cable before soldering.

Tinning the pins.

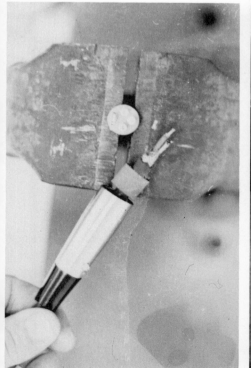

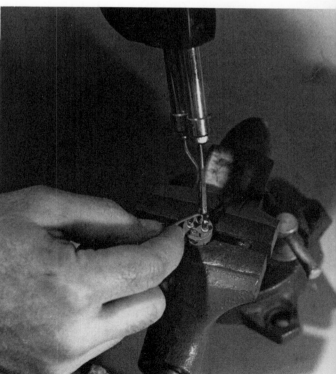

Soldering cable leads to pins: ground goes to #1;
low goes to #2; high (hot) goes to #3.

Tighten set screw to complete Cannon connector

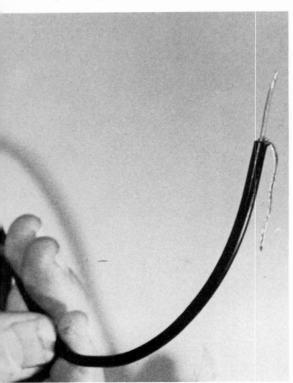

Stripped one-conductor shielded
cable with shielding folded back.

Disassembled phone plug.

Make sure shell is on
cable before soldering.

Proper placement o
cable within plug—
note position of
center conductor and g

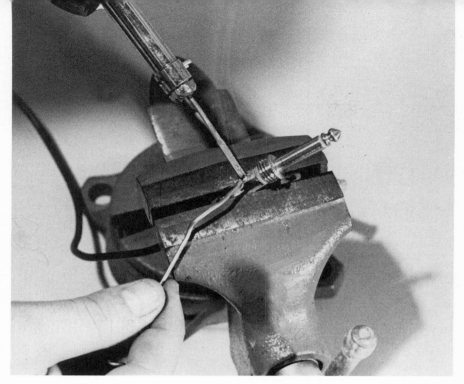

Soldering center connector to plug.

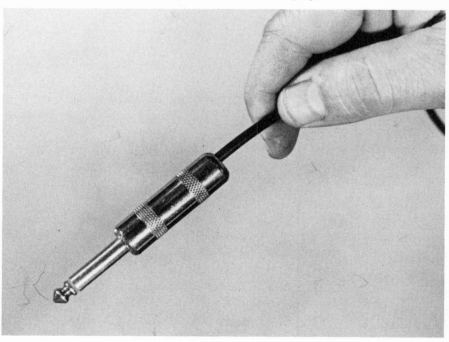

Completed phone plug.

PRESERVING VIDEO TAPE

Every manufacturer of video tape includes with his tape a guide on how to handle and store the tape. The best guide is the one prepared by Ampex Corp. This is what they recommend:

1. Never drop or bump the reels of video tape. If it is bumped, the edges of the reel can get squeezed, causing binding of the tape inside.

2. Alway normalize the temperature of the tape before putting it on a vtr. If the tape has been stored in an area that is a different temperature than the room where the vtr is, leave the tape next to the vtr for a few hours before threading it up on the machine.

3. Always lift the tape from its box by the hub or the lower flange of the reel. Lifting by the edges can cause squeezing and damage to the tape.

4. Always keep the tape clean. Never let it touch the floor or any other surface while handling or loading onto the recorder.

5. Cut off damaged and wrinkled tape ends. Threading tape with uneven ends can cause misalignment and subsequent damage to the entire reel, and to the video heads on the vtr.

6. Avoid splicing when possible. If splicing is necessary, use only special splicing tape designed for video tape. If you don't, serious head damage may result.

7. Thread the tape carefully around the guides and head drum to prevent scratches, tears, or stretching that will affect subsequent recording or playback.

8. Allow video reels to coast gently to a stop after playing or rewinding. Stopping them quickly by pressing down on the reels can cause tape-damaging "cinching" or "windows."

9. Never stop the tape in the middle of a reel without releasing the tape tension (except to "still frame"). If you do wish to "stand-by," first check the vtr operating instructions to prevent tape-damaging misoperation.

10. Never remove the tape from the guides, head drum, or capstan in the middle of a reel. This can cause permanent damage to the edges and surface. It is best to wind the tape to either reel before removing.

11. Check the tape pack, or wrap, every time you rewind the tape. Continual rewinding with too little or too much tension can cause an uneven wrap or slippage that results in tape damage.

12. Be certain that you are operating your recorder with the optimum head tip projection. Too much tip projection chews up tape, too little causes poor picture quality.

13. Keep your vtr clean. Remember, dirt and oxide buildups collected on the capstan, tape guides, and heads are an enemy of tape. Remove them frequently according to manufacturer specifications, and with approved cleaner solvents.

14. Store video tape under the same conditions of moderate temperature, humidity, and cleanliness that feel comfortable to you. Video tape stores best at 70 degrees Fahrenheit, and at 50% humidity.

15. For best long-term storage, rewind tapes end to end before storing. Do this even if you only use a portion of the tape. This will guarantee uniform tension throughout the reel.

16. Use only approved stickers or masking tape to hold down tape ends. Never use tapes with sticky substances that may leave an adhesive residue.

17. Never write on end-of-tape stickers while they are on the tape. This causes slight but permanent "dents" that transfer themselves down into many layers of tape.

18. Store video tape in its original box. Make certain that all storage boxes have a hub support so that reels do not stand on their flanges; stand the boxes upright on storage shelves. Tape should always be in one of two places: *on the recorder OR in the original box.*

THE TELEVISION SIGNAL

by Robert B. Pfannkuch

Objectives

It is the objective of this short text to supply you with basic information about the television process. With this information, you will be able to:

— examine a television signal on a waveform monitor and

— adjust most television cameras, recorders and monitors to receive the best possible television picture.

The technical nature of television is quite complex, and is often very difficult for the layman to understand. For this reason, the author will often generalize, and will frequently use analogies to avoid technical detail. As the content is very compressed, you will probably want to re-read each section a few times, to insure a complete understanding.

Overview

In a studio, television cameras convert the image of a subject into a stream of electronic information—the television signal. The signal can then be transmitted by cable directly to a monitor, converted to a radio frequency and transmitted by air to a receiver, or recorded on a videotape recorder for later transmission.

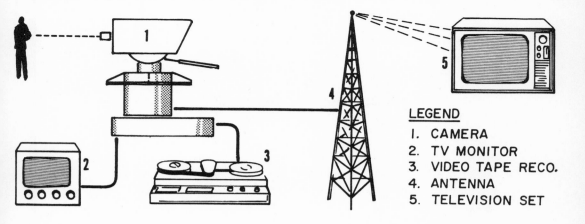

LEGEND
1. CAMERA
2. TV MONITOR
3. VIDEO TAPE RECO.
4. ANTENNA
5. TELEVISION SET

"Monitor" is the name for a television set that receives its signal only by cable (video frequency). "Receiver" is the name for a set that picks up a radio frequency signal thru its antenna.

In the receiver or monitor, the signal is converted back to a picture on the screen. Since the picture on the screen is familiar to all of us, we will begin there, and work our way back to the studio equipment that originates and records the signal.

The Television Picture

The television signal enters the monitor as a steady stream of sequential bits of electronic information. Within this stream is contained information about the picture itself, and syncronizing information which tells the monitor how to convert the signal back to a picture. In a receiver, the sound information is also mixed in with this signal, but is separated from picture and sync as soon as the signal is in the set.

Take a close look at a television screen, and you will see that the picture is made up of many horizontal lines. The incoming television signal contains all these lines, in a continuous stream. The signal is sent to an electron gun inside the picture tube where it is broken down into the individual lines. These lines are then sprayed, line by line, from left to right, and from the top of the screen to the bottom.

The coating on the inside of the picture tube glows whenever the spray strikes it. The brightness of the glow at any one point on any line depends on the strength of the signal hitting at that point. If

175

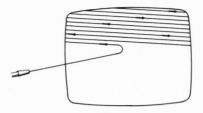

that part (element) of the picture is to be dark, the signal is weak and the screen just barely glows. If that part of the picture is to be bright, the signal is strong and that point on the screen glows brightly.

The part of the picture tube's faceplate which receives the spray from the electron gun is called the RASTER. The set's case covers the outer edges of the RASTER, and the area of the Raster exposed to the viewer is called the SCREEN.

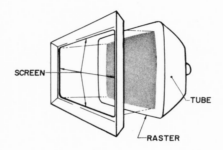

The signal entering the set is a continuous stream of bits of picture information, with synchronizing information mixed in. It is this synchronizing information which tells the electron gun inside the

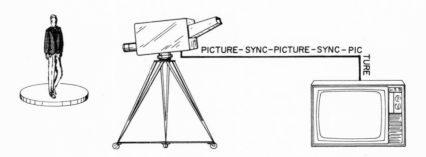

picture tube how to break up the stream into individual lines. There is a SYNC PULSE at the end of each line. When the gun encounters that pulse, it knows that it is time to begin the next line.

The gun begins on the left, and sprays a line across the screen. At the end of the line, it turns almost completely off. Then, when it encounters the sync pulse, it snaps back to the left of the Raster, turns up to normal strength, and begins spraying the next line.

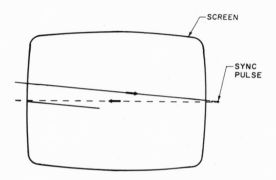

The period during which the gun is turned down (in strength) is called BLANKING. During this period, the signal sprayed is not strong enough to cause the screen to glow. This is done to prevent the returning spray from interfering with the picture just sprayed across the screen.

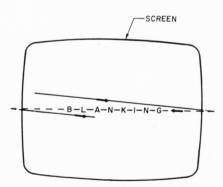

The period during blanking when the beam is actually returning to the left is called RETRACE. Notice that Blanking begins a bit before Retrace, and continues for a bit after the Retrace has been completed. We will go into detail about this in a short while.

177

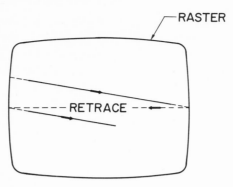

One complete spraying of the Raster, from top to bottom, consists of 262½ lines, and is called a FIELD. At the end of the last line of a Field, the electron gun encounters another type of sync pulse. This bit of sync tells the gun to return to the top of the screen, and begin spraying the first line of the next field. As it did at the end of each line, the gun turns down (BLANKING), returns to the top of the Screen (RETRACE), and begins spraying the first

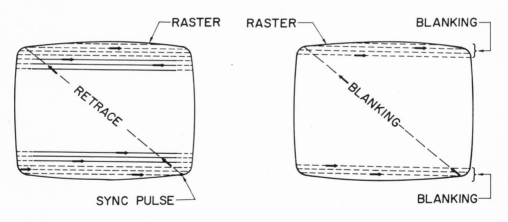

line of the next Field. Each Field takes ⅟₆₀th of a second to spray. This means that the viewer is presented with a new Field 60 times every second. The image on any screen must be interrupted at least 40-50 times every second to give the perception of motion without flicker (this rule is the same that applies to motion pictures). At the 60 Field-per-second rate, television achieves a picture with excellent fluidity of motion.

At the end of the last picture line in a Field, the gun does not go into Retrace immediately but, as it did for each line, goes into Blanking first, and remains blanked until well after the Retrace has been completed. The areas of Blanking before and after Retrace are called PORCHES. Later, when we examine the television signal on a waveform monitor, you will see why the name "porch" has been given to those parts of the signal.

There is a correct name for every part of the signal we have discussed so far.

HORIZONTAL BLANKING: The period during which the gun is turned down between LINES.

HORIZONTAL SYNC: The part of the television signal that tells the electron gun to stop spraying one line, and return to begin spraying the next LINE.

HORIZONTAL RETRACE: The period during which the gun is returning to spray the next LINE.

VERTICAL BLANKING: The period during which the gun is turned down between FIELDS.

VERTICAL SYNC: The part of the signal that tells the gun to begin spraying the next FIELD.

VERTICAL RETRACE: The period during which the gun is returning to spray the next FIELD.

The diagram below serves to visually summarize all the parts of the television signal that we have seen so far.

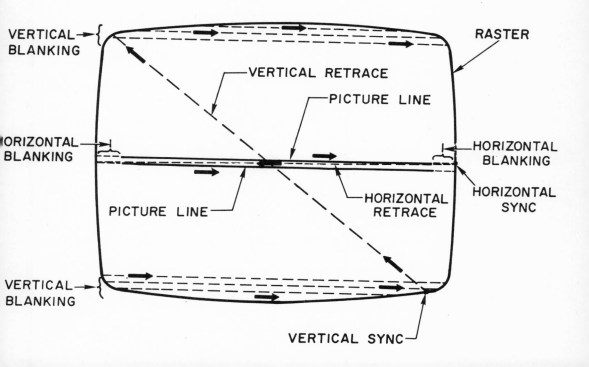

It would be pleasantly simple if that was all there was to the television signal. Unfortunately, there is more, and it begins to get a bit complex.

A single 262½ line Field is only half of a complete television picture. After the first Field has been sprayed, the gun returns to the top and begins to spray the second Field. However, the spray is slightly offset this time, so that the lines of the second Field fall BETWEEN the lines of the first Field. In the following diagram consider the heavy lines as the first Field and the thin lines as the second Field. This effect is called INTERLACE.

A high quality television system will create a POSITIVE INTER-LACE picture, where the lines of the second Field fall EXACTLY between the lines of the first. With positive interlace, every line is seen and the resulting picture is quite sharp.

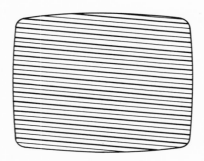

Less expensive systems create a RANDOM INTERLACE picture, where the lines of the second Field fall, at random, between (or over) the lines of the first. With random interlace, the number of lines seen varies with every Field sprayed.

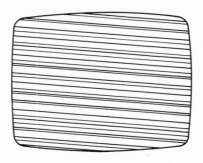

180

Two complete (and interlaced) Fields (262½ lines + 262½ lines) make up one FRAME (525 lines). A FRAME is a complete picture, and a new Frame occurs every $\frac{1}{30}$th of a second.

The term RESOLUTION is used to describe how accurately a television system can reproduce the original image. "Resolution" does not refer to the actual number of lines on the screen, but to a numerical standard against which the completeness of the picture can be measured. On the test pattern used in television there are two wedges used for measuring resolution.

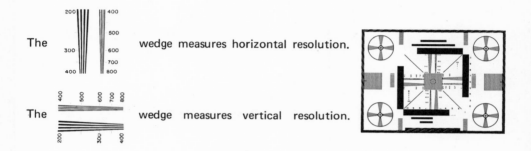

The ⌇ wedge measures horizontal resolution.

The ⌇ wedge measures vertical resolution.

As you follow each wedge toward its point, you encounter a spot at which you can no longer distinguish the individual lines. The number alongside that spot indicates the resolution.

If there is a television set near you, turn it on and adjust the vertical knob so that the picture "rolls." If you can stabilize the roll to hold between pictures, you will see a black line across the screen. Adjusting the brightness and contrast knobs will show you that this line is really a dark grey area, with a very dark line running through the middle.

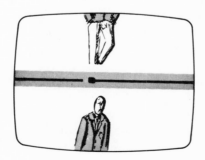

This part of the picture (normally falling below the screen and out of the viewer's sight) is the Blanking and sync information between Fields. The grey lines are the vertical BLANKING areas where the gun is spraying no picture. The dark band is the SYNC PULSE that triggers Retrace. The grey area below (after) the sync pulse is the part of Blanking after Retrace, and before the first picture line of the next Field. The projections from the vertical sync pulse are called EQUALIZING PULSES, which create the offset that causes interlace. For the purposes of this text, we need do no more than identify these equalizing pulses.

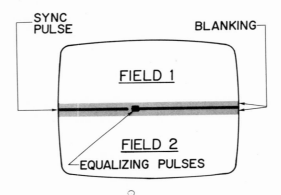

Before you proceed, compare the picture above to the summary diagram on page 179 and be sure you comfortably understand everything discussed so far.

The picture on a television screen is not an accurate enough way to examine a television signal. On the screen, we can not see the entire raster, so we can not examine the synchronizing information. The brightness and contrast knobs are variable, so we can not even measure the quality of the picture itself. The signal created in a studio must be of a very specific strength and structure, and we must have a tool that will allow us to accurately examine and measure the television signal. This device is called a WAVEFORM MONITOR.

The Waveform

An oscilloscope is a device which displays the variations of an electronic signal. A waveform monitor is a special type of oscilloscope, which displays the variations in strength and structure of a tele-

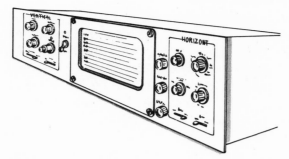

vision signal. On an waveform monitor, the signal is displayed in a form that we can use to measure how much of an entire Field (for example) is picture, how much is sync, how much is Blanking, where the sync pulse falls, and how strong (in volts) any part of this signal is at any point. Both the strength and the structure of the signal affect the quality and stability of the final picture. A video engineer uses his waveform monitor to examine the signal, then adjusts his cameras, control equipment and recorders to achieve the best possible picture.

FIELD WAVEFORM

Since the waveform representation of a field (262½ lines) is the one you will be using most often, we'll begin by studying the structure of a Field. Later, we'll briefly examine the structure of an individual line.

We have referred to the television signal as a continuous stream of information, mostly picture, with sync pulses occurring at the end of each Line, and at the end of each Field. The waveform illustrated

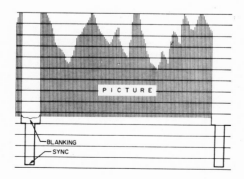

at the right shows all the parts of one Field. You can see the picture lines, the area of blanking, and the sync pulse that tells the picture tube's electron gun to begin vertical Retrace.

You can also see that the picture part of the signal varies greatly in strength, and that the Blanking portion has almost no strength. At this point, you can see why the areas of Blanking before and after the sync pulse are called PORCHES. Since the picture portion looks like a box house, the blanking areas look like the house's porches. The area of Blanking before sync is called the FRONT PORCH. The area after sync is called the BACK PORCH. The porches serve to separate picture from sync, and to give the electron gun a chance to stabilize before it reaches sync, and again before it has to spray the first line of picture.

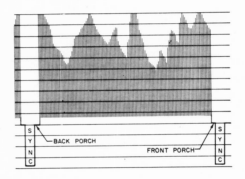

As a base of measurement, we will consider the blanking lines, (the porches) as being zero voltage (no information being sprayed). Now we can measure the relative strength of any part of picture or sync by seeing how much below or above zero (blanking) it occurs.

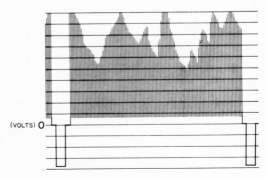

184

The faceplate of every waveform monitor has a scale printed on
it. The waveform is positioned so that the blanking line falls on the
"O" line of the scale. The 100% line then shows the strongest level
(brightest picture) that should occur anywhere in the picture portion
of the signal. The sync pulse always must fall below O.

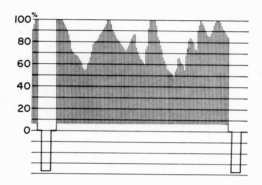

The strength of the picture part of the signal varies from almost
0 volts to .7 volts. The bottom part of the picture signal, near zero,
is black (tube does not glow). The top part, at or near .7 (or 100%)
is peak white (brightest possible glow). .7 volts is the strength
necessary to make the faceplate of the picture tube glow at maximum
brightness. If any part of the picture falls too far above .7 volts
(100%), it is too strong. Later, we will see how cameras and recorders
can be adjusted to achieve a perfect .7 volt picture strength.

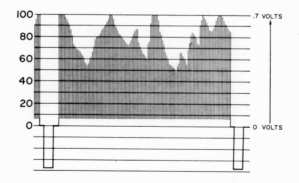

The Blanking line is zero voltage. Everything above zero (up
to .7 volts, or 100%) is positive signal and is picture. The sync pulses
fall BELOW zero, and are negative. As long as it is receiving a

positive signal, the electron gun will spray it as picture. As soon as it encounters a negative (sync) pulse, it reacts by stopping the spray and starting retrace. The proper position for the sync pulse, on the waveform is .3 volts BELOW zero. Our use of the terms "positive" and "negative" refer to + or − the waveform's blanking line, not + or − ground. As you can now see, the waveform monitor shows us all parts of the composite (picture + sync) television signal.

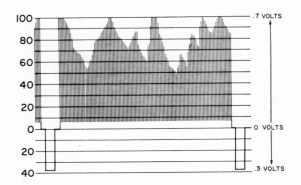

The waveform below is typical; it shows all the component parts of the signal. Be sure you understand everything about the waveform that you have seen so far, before proceeding to the next section.

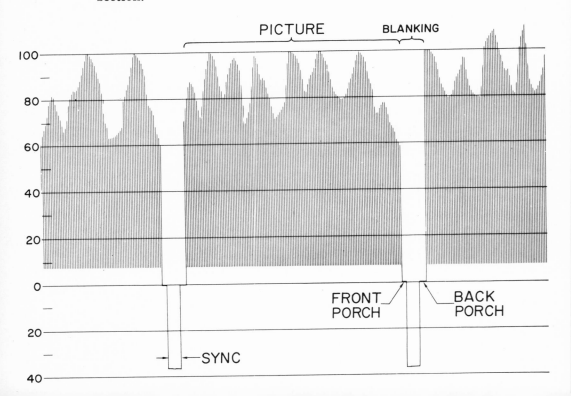

The person adjusting a television camera uses a waveform monitor as a guide. The camera controls affect only the picture, blanking and (sometimes) sync levels. The relative amount of space taken up by picture, porch and sync can be adjusted only by a highly trained video engineer.

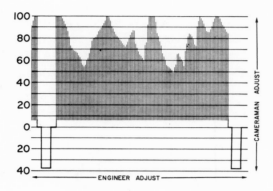

LINE WAVEFORM

Should a technician so desire, he can flip a switch on his waveform monitor and examine a single horizontal line. As you can see, a waveform representation of a line is very similar to that of a Field. This waveform shows us every part of an individual line, and is used to examine the line's sync and blanking information.

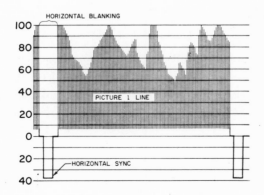

187

The Television Camera

All cameras are alike in that they see a picture, and convert it to another form. Still and movie cameras convert the image (chemically) to a picture on film. Television cameras convert the picture to an electronic signal. However, some variables are common to all cameras (still, movie and television), so let's examine these variables first. In all cameras, the light bouncing off an object is gathered by a lens, and is focused inside the camera. The brighter the light on the object, the stronger the image that is formed inside the camera. The basic measurement of light is the FOOT CANDLE. The greater the amount of light the higher the foot candle reading on an exposure meter.

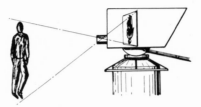

All lenses have an aperture (hole) which can be varied in size. The smaller the aperture, the less light allowed to pass thru the lens. The size of the aperture is indicated by the F STOP number on the lens.

As you can see, the larger the F STOP number, the SMALLER the hole.

f 3.5   f 4   f 5.6   f 8   f 11   f 16   f 22

In addition to controlling the strength of the entering light, the F stop also controls the DEPTH OF FIELD. When the camera is focused on a subject, the area in front of and behind that subject that is ALSO in focus is called the DEPTH OF FIELD. When you see a photograph where the photographer has purposely thrown a confusing background out of focus, he has actually adjusted his F stop to give a limited depth of field. Since the background falls beyond the depth of Field, it is not in focus. As you can see below,

188

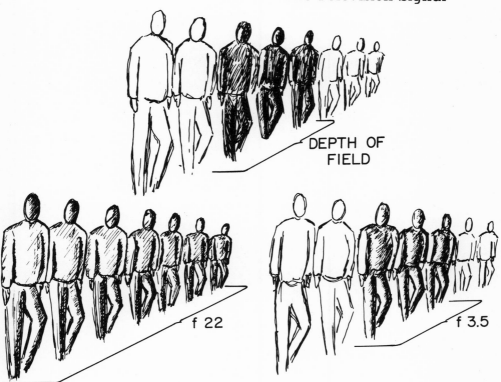

DEPTH OF FIELD

f 22

f 3.5

the SMALLER the aperture (or larger the stop reading), the greater the Depth of Field.

If the cameraman wants as much as possible to be in focus, he will close his lens to a smaller aperture (high F stop number).

If the cameraman is using a zoom lens, depth of field is very important. The cameraman must have enough depth of field to keep in focus throughout a zoom.

So far, we have seen two variables that are common to all cameras:

—the amount of light striking the subject and

—the size of the aperture.

From this point on, there is little similarity between still or movie cameras, and television cameras.

The following pages cover almost all the camera controls available. However, an individual camera does not necessarily have ALL these controls.

THE STRENGTH OF THE SIGNAL

In a television camera, the image from the lens is focused on a light sensitive faceplate inside the camera's tube, and produces an electronic reaction on that faceplate. The image on the faceplate is constantly scanned by a beam inside the tube. The image scanned by the beam is converted to an electronic signal (which contains all the information about the picture). As you can now see, the electron gun in the television set's picture tube is spraying back this signal in the same way as it was originally scanned inside the camera. The sync pulses are usually added to the picture signal AFTER that signal leaves the camera.

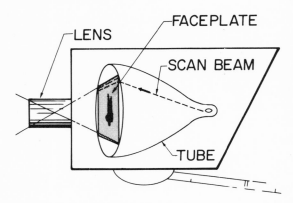

CAMERA

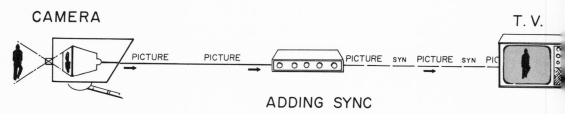

ADDING SYNC

Target

When we discussed the quantity of light hitting the subject and the aperture size, we saw those two variables as affecting the strength of the light entering the lens. Our first television camera variable is in the sensitivity of the tube's faceplate. By increasing or decreasing the voltage to this faceplate, we can increase or decrease its reaction to the light striking it. It we have too little light and/or if the aperture must be closed down for greater depth of

190

field, there may not be enough light coming thru to generate a good picture.

If there is not enough light entering (and this will show on the Waveform monitor), the cameraman can increase the voltage to the faceplate by adjusting the TARGET CONTROL. When this is done, the faceplate becomes more sensitive, and reacts more strongly to the light hitting it. With the TARGET control, we are into the first of the electronic ways of adjusting the signal. However, as we electronically adjust the signal, we begin to encounter two undesirable effects: noise and lag.

Noise

Every electronic system generates within itself a certain amount of unwanted but unavoidable miscellaneous information, called NOISE. This noise gets mixed in with the desired information, the SIGNAL, and if there is too much noise, the picture quality diminishes. In a concert hall, for example, there is a constant amount of unwanted noise (coughing, whispering, etc.) that is very noticable until the music starts. If the music is loud, the noise is almost completely drowned out by the music (or SIGNAL). The relation between the strength of the signal and the strength of the noise is called the SIGNAL TO NOISE RATIO.

In a television camera, the light entering thru the lens is pure (noise free) signal. The more electronic adjusting we do to that signal, the more noise we add to it. Hence, as we vary the target voltage, we also vary the noise mixed into the signal, and we might decrease the clarity of the resulting picture. The "snow" seen on the television screens is a good example of noise. Both too little or too much Target voltage will produce noticable noise.

| PURE NOISE | HIGH NOISE | LOW NOISE |

191

Lag

On inexpensive cameras (low priced vidicons, for example), the bright parts of the image will tend to temporarily burn into the tube's faceplate. Whenever the camera or the subject moves, the brighter parts of the picture remain burned in, and cause a smearing effect, or a ghost. As we increase the faceplate's sensitivity (with the TARGET control), we also increase its tendency to lag.

Aware of the above, it is obvious that the stronger the light entering the lens, the less target adjusting necessary and the better (least noise and lag) the picture. The TARGET control is quite sensitive. It also takes the cameraman some time to strike the best compromise between lighting, depth of field, noise and lag. For these reasons, it is best to set this control once, for normal studio lighting conditions, and then leave it alone.

Beam

The Target control increases the voltage to the tube's faceplate. The BEAM control affects the strength of the beam which is scanning that faceplate. Every time the cameraman changes the Target, he disturbs the voltage relationship between the faceplate and the scanning beam. To re-establish this relationship the BEAM control is adjusted.

Every time the Target voltage is increased, details will wash out in the white areas.

The BEAM control is then adjusted until the washout of detail in the white areas is eliminated.

192

Video Gain

Once the beam has scanned the faceplate and created the signal, that signal passes thru the camera. However, before it leaves the camera it can again be boosted with the VIDEO GAIN (or Contrast) control. This control is the one most frequently used to make minor adjustments in the strength of the signal. Although VIDEO GAIN does not affect lag, it is another means of electronic boosting, and, as such, does add noise to the picture.

On his waveform monitor, the video engineer sets the blanking line at zero on the scale, and then adjusts TARGET and VIDEO GAIN (as well as the lights and the camera's F stop), until he achieves a clear, lag free signal that is .7 volts strong at its brightest part.

THE STRUCTURE OF THE SIGNAL

Having achieved the desired signal strength, the cameraman now adjusts the structure of the signal.

Pedestal

Let's go back to our waveform representation for a moment. The lower part of the picture signal is the black or dark grey points on the screen, and the upper part shows white and light grey. If you

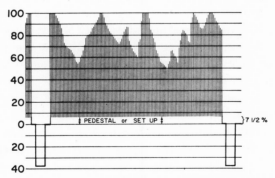

examine this waveform, you will notice that the darkest part of the picture falls slightly above the blanking line. The distance between the blanking lines and the darkest part of the picture is called the PEDESTAL or SET UP, and is controlled by the camera's PEDESTAL control. Under normal conditions, the SET UP should take up 7½% of the distance between zero (blanking line) and .7

volts (peak white). On most waveform monitors, there is a scale marking to help you measure this distance. At this 7½% level, the camera will have a normal sensitivity to blacks and dark greys. There are times when you might want to alter the set up away from the 7½% level. If you are shooting a superimposition card, an adjustment of the PEDESTAL control can make the camera less sensitive to shades of dark grey, and help achieve a white on pure black picture.

THE CAMERA'S REACTIONS

In addition to controlling the strength and the structure of the signal, there are other adjustments that affect the camera's reaction to changes in the incoming picture.

White Peak Clip

The WHITE PEAK CLIP control stops the camera from accepting any signal stronger than the selected level. If your subject constantly has glaring white spots, this control can be used to preselect a maximum white peak strength, above which the signal will not be accepted.

Gamma

The human eye does not react to severe changes in light in direct proportion to the changes. If you are in a darkened room, and the light level suddenly increases 200%, your eye will not react to the full 200% but will adjust only up to a tolerable level. Your eye, in effect, becomes less sensitive to light as the incoming light increases. Conversely, your eye becomes more sensitive to light as the light level decreases.

The GAMMA control on a camera performs a similiar function. Television cameras are normally made to be slightly oversensitive to low light situations and undersensitive in extremely bright situations. The GAMMA control allows you to adjust this sensitivity curve.

Reverse Polarity

The final control is used in special applications. The signal coming from a television camera shows black as black and white as white. However, there are times when one might want a reversal of the signal where blacks are white and whites are black (like a photograph negative). Flipping the REVERSE POLARITY switch accomplishes this change.

194

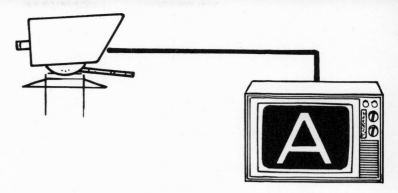

Title cards, for example, must have white lettering on a black background in order to be superimposed over another picture. However, if your camera has a REVERSE POLARITY switch, you can type black lettering on a white card, then reverse the camera's polarity to produce the white on black result.

FOCUS

Television cameras have three focus controls:

OPTICAL FOCUS: There is a focus ring on every lens, usually marked off in feet or meters. In normal use, the optical focus should be set to the marking corresponding to the distance from the camera to the subject.

MECHANICAL FOCUS: This adjustment, usually found on the back of the camera, moves the tube closer to or further from the lens. With the optical focus set for the proper distance, the mechanical focus is adjusted to achieve the clearest possible picture.

ELECTRONIC FOCUS: The electronic focus adjustment on the camera pinpoints the beam which scans the tube's faceplate, and is used last to sharpen the picture.

When focusing on an extremely close object, the lens focus is set to the closest distance marking, and the mechanical focus is adjusted (moving the tube closer to the lens) until a sharp picture is obtained. In such cases, the camera is so far from its normal focus arrangement that the depth of field will be very narrow, and the slightest change in distance will throw the picture out of focus.

When using a zoom lens, the cameraman

—zooms on to his tightest (closest) shot and adjusts the OPTICAL focus for a sharp picture then

—zooms back for his furthest shot and adjusts the MECHANICAL focus.

If he has enough depth of field, this procedure will then allow

195

him to zoom in and out, and maintain focus at all times. If he cannot hold focus thru the zoom, he will have to close down the aperture (for more depth of field) and adjust Target or Video Gain to bring the signal back up to .7 volts strength.

THE SYNC SIGNAL

The sync pulses are added AFTER the picture signal has been created and electronically boosted. Some cameras add sync to the picture signal, while other cameras rely on an outside sync generator to add sync.

The SYNC LEVEL adjustment on the camera or on the sync generator controls the strength of the sync pulses. As was shown in the section on the Waveform Monitor, the sync pulses should have a strength of .3 volts BELOW the blanking line.

TEST PATTERN

A standard TEST PATTERN is the best tool to use when setting up a camera. The Test Pattern should be put into normal studio

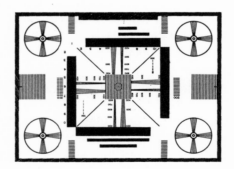

lighting. The camera is then focused on the pattern so that the pattern fills the entire screen. The PEDESTAL control is set to the 7½% level, and the studio monitors adjusted so that the pattern's GREY SCALES show the most graduations between black and white.

The Optical focus is set to the distance between pattern and camera, then the Mechanical and Electronic focus is set to the converging lines (wedges) are as sharp and distant as possible. All the studio monitors can then be adjusted for maximum clarity.

196

Additional Information

60 CYCLE HUM

If the waveform shows a wavy, instead of straight, Blanking line, there is a 60 cycle hum in the system. This can usually be corrected by proper grounding of the system.

VIDEOTAPE RECORDERS VIDEO GAIN

By the time the signal gets into the VTR, it is a composite signal (.7 volts picture + .3 volts sync). All recorders have a VIDEO GAIN control which is adjusted until the VTR's meter reads 100%. This means that the recorder is recording a composite one volt (.7 + .3) signal.

If either part of the incoming signal is not at proper strength, the VTR's Video Gain should NOT be used to correct the situation. Since the incoming signal is composite, increasing the VTR's Video Gain will affect BOTH picture and sync levels. If, for example, the incoming signal is only .4 volts picture, but .3 volts sync, increasing the VTR Video Gain will increase both the picture and the sync levels. Increased to 100%, you will have almost enough picture but far too much sync.

Therefore, using a waveform monitor, you should adjust both picture and sync levels at their source (camera and sync generator), rather than adjusting the VTR's Video Gain.

DUBBING FROM VTR TO VTR

When copying a tape from one recorder to another, you must make certain that the signal being transferred is a composite of .7 picture and .3 sync. This can be checked with a Waveform Monitor. To correct an already recorded but imperfect signal, a PROCESSING AMPLIFIER should be used.

The original signal is fed into the processing amplifier, where picture and sync are separated. Each part is re-amplified to its proper strength, and the two parts are rejoined to make a proper composite signal. The processed signal is then fed into the other recorder.

SINGLE HEAD VIDEOTAPE RECORDERS

Videotape recorders with only one head produce a signal with

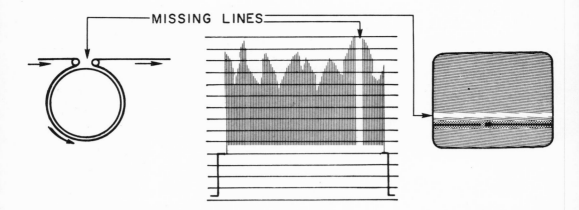

a particular characteristic. Since the tape cannot wrap around the head drum a full 360 degrees, there must be a short time during each revolution when the head leaves the tape. This means that a few lines will be missing from each Field. These missing lines are not, per se, any disadvantage.

In fact, processing amplifiers can be purchased which will add the missing lines to the signal coming out of a recorder.

It is important, however, that these missing lines fall where the manufacturer specifies. They should fall either at the top or at the bottom of the Raster, and outside of the viewing area (Screen). By using your waveform monitor, you can see where these missing lines fall. If they do not fall where the manufacturer specifies, a technician should be called to correct the situation. Accurate placement of these missing lines is critical when making dubs or kinescopes.

Conclusion

It may take a few readings of this and other texts, and a lot of experience with your own equipment, to master basic television theory and operation. The better you understand the tools with which you have to work, the better the results will be and the more television will be able to do for you.

Aware of the technical liberties we have taken for the sake of simplicity, we want to remind you that this text is conceptual overview, not a definitive technical manual. If you wish to pursue the technical aspects of television in greater detail, we suggest that you read Donald Fink's "The Television Signal," available from University Microfilms.

198

GLOSSARY

This glossary contains terms that were used in the book, as well as some that were not. It is not meant to be the ultimate collection of video terms, but it does contain those items that you will use most often in portable electrography.

AC: Alternating Current, normal home 110/120 volts.

Acetate: Transparent plastic sheet used in graphics, cellulose acetate. Also, film base.

Ad Lib: Unrehearsed action or dialogue.

Animation: Artificially created apparent motion imparted by frame-by-frame method in film and video.

Aperture: F-stop, opening of lens diaphragm.

Arc: Curved camera movement in the shape of an arc.

Aspect Ratio: Ratio between the height and width of a television picture. Three units high by four units wide, 3:4.

Atmosphere: Creation of a mood to make a scene appear more real.

Audio: The sound portion of the visual program. The audio range for the human ear is 20 to 20,000 cycles per second.

Background: A set or sound used behind or below the action to help create an effect of realism.

Back Light: Light directed at object from behind, the side facing away from the camera.

Balance: A pleasing picture composition, or well mixed audio.

Barndoors: Adjustable metal shades mounted on the front of a spotlight to control the extent of the light beam.

Beam: The flow of electrons emitted from an electron gun in a television set or camera.

Black: Screen that has no picture information showing on it, a blank screen.

Boom: Long-armed device that can suspend a microphone in the air above a performer.

199

Broad: Rectangular-shaped floodlight, whose light beam can be partially controlled.

Broadcast: The transmission of electronic signals by means of a Radio Frequency (RF) over the air waves. Also, professional television equipment classification.

Bulk Eraser: An electronic device used to erase entire reel of tape at one time.

Burn-In: Image impregnated onto camera pickup tube, caused by extremely bright light, or camera focused on high-contrast image for too long a period of time. The tube will retain a negative image of this supered over other objects that the camera is seeing.

Busy: Picture or sound that is very cluttered or crowded.

Camera: Device that contains lens, pickup tube, and other electronic equipment that changes light into an electronic signal for television.

Camera Left and Right: Stage directions given from camera point of view.

Cap: A rubber or metal cover that protects the lens.

Capstan: Roller that keeps tape moving through a video tape recorder at a constant speed.

Cardioid: Heart-shaped pickup pattern of a microphone.

CATV: Community Antenna Television, or Cable television. One master antenna feeds an entire community with broadcast and closed circuit programs, via coaxial cable.

CCTV: Closed Circuit television. Similar to CATV, but on smaller scale. Usually used in a school or business.

Chroma-Key: Electronic special effect, similar to mat. Only in color television, since it uses the blue wavelength.

Cinching: Slippage between layers of video tape in rewinding or fast forward on a video tape recorder.

Close-up: Very tight shot, object shown at close range.

Coaxial Cable, or *Coax:* Specially designed shielded cable used to transmit television signals.

Compatibility: The ability of one electronic piece of equipment to interface with another. The tapes made on some vtr's are not interchangeable with other vtr's; they will not be able to be shown on any vtr that is not compatible with the one on which the tape was recorded.

Composite: Picture signal made up of video and sync information.

Contrast: Relationship between light and dark elements of a picture. High contrast has extremes of light and dark, low contrast has middle tones.

Control Room: Room from which operations in a television studio are directed and controlled.

Cover Shot: Wide-angle establishing shot, sets the scene by giving proper orientation.

Cue: A visual or audible signal that starts the action in a scene.

Crawl: Graphics that move across the screen.

Credits: List of the names of the people that participated in the creation of a program.

CU: Close-up.

Cut: Instant switch from one camera to another. Or an order to stop the action.

Cyc: Cyclorama, curtain that curves around rear of set.

Degauss: To demagnetize.

Depth of Field: The area between the closest and farthest objects that are in focus at a particular F-stop.

Decibel, or *"db":* Unit measure of sound volume or strength.

Directional: Particular pickup pattern of microphone.

Director: Person responsible for all camera movement and actor movement during television production. Coordinates all production elements.

Dimmer: Controls the brightness of a light.

Dissolve: Transition between two pictures, one fades out while the next fades in; they overlap for a period. Can also apply to audio.

Dolly: Moving camera toward object (dolly-in) or away (dolly-out).

Dropout: Loss of signal during tape playback or record because of tape/head separation. Horizontal streaks of black or white that appear on the screen.

Dub: Electronic copying of recorded information.

Dynamic: Pressure-sensitive microphone, very popular in television production.

EIA: Electronic Industries Assoc. Establishes standards for television equipment.

EIAJ: EIA of Japan. Promoted standarization in half-inch video tape format.

Edit: Process of putting together program material in a desired order.

Electronic Edit: Process of adding material to a tape without splicing the tape. "Assemble" edit is the addition of information to a tape. An "insert" edit puts information between existing taped material.

Electron Gun: Device that sprays beam of electrons at faceplate of pickup tube in a camera, or at the raster in a receiver.

Ellipsoidal Spot: Spotlight with highly controllable light pattern.

Erasure: neutralizing of magnetic field on magnetic tape, loss of information.

ETV: Educational television.

Fade: Increase or decrease in video or audio level.

Feed: Transmission of television signal from origination point to termination point.

Feedback: In audio—high-pitched squeal resulting from reamplification of sound between microphone and amplifier. In video—image produced when camera is aimed at a monitor that is showing its own signal. The effects are lines and flashes that can be controlled with practice, to produce special effects.

Field: One complete scan of the faceplate or raster. 262½ lines of picture information, or half of a frame.

Fill Light: Lighting designed to soften shadows.

Film Chain: A device that can show a film on television with no flickering. Consists of a television camera and a special film projector.

Flip Stand: Rack that holds graphics in position.

Floodlight: Lighting instrument that throws out nondirectional diffused beam.

Focal Length: Distance from optical center of lens to faceplate of pickup tube in camera.

Focus: Optical—point at which light coming in through lens forms sharp clear lines on faceplate. Electronic—sharpest image obtainable by adjusting optics and the beam in the pickup tube.

Follow focus: Maintaining focus on a moving object by adjusting focus ring on lens.

Foot Candle: International unit of measuring light. The amount of light produced at one foot away on a surface, by an average candle.

Format: General makeup of a television script or program.

Frame: One complete television picture. 525 lines of picture information. Two fields.

Freon: Head-cleaning solution.

Frequency Response: Expressed in the range of the potential db difference.

F-stop: Calibration on lens, marking position of diaphragm. Large F-stop means small opening, small F-stop means larger opening of diaphragm.

Full Script: Script that contains all picture and audio information.

Gain: Level of amplified sound or video.

Generation: Denotes how far removed from the original, or "first generation," a tape is. The first copy is the second generation, the copy of that tape is the third generation, etc.

Gen-Lock: Locking up of the sync generators of two different sources.

Glitch: Video-slang for any picture imperfection.

Graphics: Any stills inserted into a television program such as title cards, charts, slides, photographs, etc.

Gray Scale: Shades of gray to which all colors correspond on a television screen. There are seven- and ten-step scales.

Halo: Flare of light around edges of very bright object on screen.

Head: Device that transfers information to the tape from video tape recorder in the record mode, and vice versa in playback.

Helical Scan: Recording format in which information is put on tape in a slanting or diagonal pattern; also called "Slant Track."

Image Orthicon, or *I-O:* Very high-quality television pickup tube.

Impedance: Rating of the electrical characteristics of electronic components. Either "high" or "low."

Iris: Same as diaphragm.

Interlace: System of sync that insures that the lines of the second field will fall between the lines of the first field.

Jack: Female cable connector.

Joy Stick: Lever that positions particular special effect on the screen, usually used with a circle.

Key Light: Main source of illumination in a scene.

Kinescope, or *"Kine":* Television picture recorded on film from a kinescope tube.

Lavaliere: Small microphone worn around neck.
Lens: Combination of layers of ground glass that has a specific focal length. Used to project image onto faceplate of pickup tube.
Level: Measure of the strength of audio and video signals.
Lighting: The illumination of a scene, made up of front (key) light, back light, and side light (fill).
Light level: Intensity of light in foot candles.
Line: Main program source, final picture that is fed to the vtr, seen on line monitor.
Lip Sync: Person's lips move at same time the words are heard.
Live: Camera or microphone that is turned on, or program transmitted at same time as it takes place.
Long Shot, or *"LS":* Shot that has very wide field of view.

Master: First-generation tape, or edited version from which dubs will be made.
Microphone, Mic, or *Mike:* Instrument that converts sound waves to electrical pulses.
Mixer: Device that mixes audio signals such as mikes and/or phonographs.
Monitor: Television set that receives only the video signal, usually has high resolving ability.
MS: Medium shot, covers range of shots between long shots and close-ups.
Multiplexer: Movable mirrors or prism set up in such a way that it can direct slide projectors and film projectors into a television camera. Similar to film chain, but has additional sources.

Narrator: Off-camera voice on sound track.
Negative Image: Reversed polarity of picture. White is black, and vice versa.
Noise: Unwanted video information. Generated by any electrical system. Looks like "snow" on screen.
Normal Lens: Lens which provides angle of view similar to that of the human eye. Normal lens for a vidicon camera is 25 mm.

204

Oscilloscope: Device used for alignment of electronic signals. Shows patterns on a display screen.

Oxide: Magnetic particles coated onto video tape, one kind of formula.

Pan: Moving the camera to the right or left in a swivelling motion.

Patch: Interconnect cables, either video or audio.

Peaks: Highest levels of signal strength as seen on VU meters and video level meters.

Pickup Tube: Electron tube, either I-O, Plumbicon, or vidicon, where image is focused from the lens onto the faceplate of the tube.

Pot: Potentiometer, volume control knob or dial.

Preamplifier: "Preamp" raises weak signals high enough so that they may be fed into an amplifier.

Print Through: Method of duplicating tapes, where a mirror image is obtained via a magnetic induction passing over two tapes that are touching one another.

Quartz-Iodine: Very efficient, very bright, long-lasting bulb used in lighting instruments.

Random Interlace: Unstable form of sync pulses that produce poor picture quality. The two fields may show the same or different lines of picture information; the fields do not necessarily fit between one another.

Raster: Face of the picture tube that picks up the stream of electrons from the electron gun, coated with particles that will glow to create a picture. Contains the screen.

Rear Screen Projection, "RP": Image projected onto back of translucent screen, usually slides or film, and picked up in the front.

Receiver: Television set that receives RF signals, a home-type set.

Receiver/Monitor: Television set whose function can be changed from one mode to the other.

Reel: Film or tape spool.

Retention: The capability of the eye to keep an image on the retina for a fraction of a second. This allows film and television to create the illusion of motion.

Resolution: Measurement of the degree of detail that a piece of television equipment is capable of reproducing.

Remote: Broadcast television term meaning a production that does not take place in a studio. All Porta-Pak programs are remotes.

Run-Through: Rehearsal.

RF: Modulated video/sync/audio signal at a particular frequency.

RF Converter: Small modulator which will drive a receiver directly from a vtr.

Scanning: The movement of the electron beam from top to bottom, and left to right.

Scene: The setting of a shot; or one shot; or a sequence of shots.

Scoop: Large floodlight.

Semiscript: Script that only partially describes audio and video portions of a program.

Set: Surroundings in a scene as seen by a television camera.

Shading: Contrast adjustment.

Signal to Noise Ratio, S/N: Ratio of power of picture signal to the inherent noise in a system.

Slant Track: see Helical Scan.

Snow: Electronic interference in a picture, "noise."

Solid State: Use of transistors instead of tubes.

Special Effects: Electronic and mechanical devices to create different illusions on the screen.

Splice: Physical joining of two pieces of tape.

Spot Light: Type of lighting instrument that produces narrow beam.

Stability: Measure of vtr or camera's life-like abilities. Straight lines should appear straight; there should be no pulsating in the overall picture. The actual quality of the picture produced by the camera or vtr.

Still Frame: "Freeze Frame"—vtr scans one field continuously; the picture quality is only half that of a frame, but handy for reference.

Storyboard: Drawings of video next to audio in a comic strip fashion, that detail all elements of a program. A visual script.

Strike: Remove or dismantle scenery.

Superimpose, Super: the overlapping, simultaneous showing of two or more pictures on one screen.

Sync: The synchronization pulses that keep all television equipment in one circuit pulsing at the same time, to keep them in phase with one another.

Supply Reel: Reel from which tape comes when going through a vtr.

Take-up Reel: Same size as supply reel, takes up tape from supply reel after the tape has gone through the vtr.

Tally Light: Red light on camera that goes on when that camera is on the "line."

Tape: Extremely thin plastic, one-quarter to two inches wide. Oxide formula on one side receives magnetic information from heads.

Tape Guides: Grooved pins that guide tape around head assembly.

Target: Light-sensitive faceplate of pickup tube.

Telephoto: Lens that has long focal length, enlarges objects, has narrow field of view.

Termination: Resistance at the end of any video signal, always 75 ohms, in video.

Test Pattern: Special design of circles and lines that is used to properly focus and align television cameras.

Tilt: Moving the camera vertically up or down.

Truck: Movement of the camera and tripod/dolly laterally, to the left or right.

Two Shot: A shot that frames two people or any two objects.

Turret: Mounting for up to four lenses on front of camera.

UHF: Ultra High Frequency, channels 14 through 83.

VHF: Very High Frequency, channels 2 through 13.

Video: The picture portion of the television signal. Also, generic term used to mean television.

Video Tape: Magnetic tape specifically designed to pickup, store, and play back television signals.

Vidicon: Pickup tube that is used on Porta-Pak systems, long-lasting and durable.

Viewfinder: Small monitor built in or attached to top of camera, that allows cameraman to see what his camera is picking up. Also, optical viewfinders, not as accurate but cheaper.

Voice Over, or "VO": Same as Narration.

VU Meter: Volume Unit Meter, measures audio levels.

VTR: Video Tape Recorder, device that transfers video, audio, and sync information onto video tape, for later playback.

Making the Media Revolution

Wavelength: Actual length of tape needed to record one cycle of a signal, or length of one signal-cycle.

Wipe: Special effect, electronic or mechanical, that appears to "push" one image off the screen with another image, either vertically or horizontally.

Wow: Distortion in tape speed causing audio distortion, usually found at start of tape, before tape gets up to recording speed.

XCU: Extreme close-up.

Zoom Lens: A lens that has a variable focal length. Referred to by the limits of the focal length range, a 15mm to 150mm lens is a 10 to 1 (10:1) zoom lens.

REFERENCES

Efrein, Joel L., *Video Tape Production and Communication Techniques,* Tab Books, Blue Ridge Summit, Pa., 1971.

Mattingly, Grayson, and Smith, Welby, *Introducing the Single Camera VTR System,* S and M Productions, Washington, D.C., 1971.

McLuhan, Marshall, *Understanding Media; The Extensions of Man,* McGraw-Hill, New York, 1964.

Shamberg, Michael, *Guerrilla Television,* Holt, Rhinehart and Winston, New York, 1971.

Smallman, Kirk, *Creative Film-Making,* Macmillan, New York, 1969.

Zettl, Herbert, *Television Production Handbook,* 2d ed., Wadsworth, Belmont, Calif., 1968.

INDEX

Index

212

Index

Index

216